Kama Sutra
SUPER SEX

Kama Sutra

DISCOVER EROTIC BLISS WEEK BY WEEK

SUPER SEX

NICOLE BAILEY

DUNCAN BAIRD PUBLISHERS

LONDON

KAMA SUTRA SUPER SEX
NICOLE BAILEY

First published in the United Kingdom and Ireland in 2009 by
Duncan Baird Publishers Ltd
Sixth Floor, Castle House, 75–76 Wells Street
London W1T 3QH

Conceived, created and designed by Duncan Baird Publishers

Managing Editor: Grace Cheetham
Editor: Dawn Bates
Managing Designer: Manisha Patel
Designer: Saskia Janssen
Commissioned Photography: John Davis

British Library Cataloguing-in-Publication Data:
A CIP record for this book is available from the British Library

ISBN: 978-1-84483-787-8

10 9 8 7 6 5 4 3 2 1

Typeset in Gill Sans and Nofret
Colour reproduction by Scanhouse, Malaysia
Printed in Hong Kong by Imago

PUBLISHERS' NOTE:
The publishers, the author and the photographer cannot accept any responsibility
for any injuries or damages incurred as a result of following the advice in this book,
or of using any of the techniques described or mentioned herein. If you suffer from
any health problems or special conditions, it is recommended that you consult your
doctor before following any practice suggested in this book. Some of the advice in
this book involves the use of massage oil. However, do not use massage oil if you are
using a condom – the oil damages latex.

CONTENTS

INTRODUCTION

Do you want to anticipate, savour and extract the fullest possible enjoyment from sex? Would you like to experience more intimate and fulfilling lovemaking? If so, there can be no greater inspiration than the *Kama Sutra*. Despite dating back to 1–4CE, this – and other erotic texts – still give us some of our best, most inspiring sources of sex positions, techniques, rites and rituals. The *Kama Sutra*'s author, Vatsyayana Mallanga, considered sex to be an art and sensuality to be "as important to the well-being of the body as food."

OLD AND NEW

Kama Sutra Super Sex mixes ancient wisdom with contemporary knowledge about sex. There are 52 sensual and erotic positions – one for each week of the year – taken from the ancient sex-texts and combined with contemporary sexpertise. For example, how to target her G-spot, how to move to delay climax, or how to adjust a position to heighten clitoral stimulation.

The sexual temperature gets hotter with every chapter: Melting Sensuality focuses on positions that offer a sensual connection; Erotic Sensations on those that maximize sexual sensations; Pure Pleasure features positions that offer an intense erotic charge; and Ultimate Turn-Ons explores more adventurous ways of having sex.

ANCIENT TEXTS

The sex positions are drawn not just from the *Kama Sutra* but also from the *Ananga Ranga* and *The Perfumed Garden*. Like the *Kama Sutra*, the *Ananga Ranga* is an erotic classic that originated in India. It was written in the 15th century by Kalyana Malla as a sex guide for husbands to help keep eroticism alive in marriage. *The Perfumed Garden*, from 16th-century Tunis, was another guide intended to help lovers to maintain a sexual charge. Positions from Chinese Taoist sexology also feature; these are said to harmonize the masculine and feminine energies of yin and yang.

ADDED PLEASURE

In between the sizzling sex positions, you'll find pages on how to enhance your lovemaking.

Kama Sutra Wisdom: Discover the techniques, advice and fascinating sexual insights given in this ancient text and how to adapt them to modern-day lovemaking.

Sensual Pleasure: Find out how to kiss, caress, massage and play with your lover to up the eroticism and intimacy of your sexual experience.

Mind Sex: Play with your lover's mind as well as their body by sharing your fantasies, trying role-play, communicating your sexual needs and getting in the right mood for sex.

Try Tantra: Tantra is the ancient Indian art of lovemaking in which you and your lover harness sexual energy to reach a heightened state. If you practise the Tantra exercises sequentially, you'll have the equivalent of a beginner's class.

So enjoy dipping in to this book and together you and your lover can experiment, learn and enjoy the ultimate in sexual fulfilment, *Kama Sutra*-style.

MELTING SENSUALITY

1

THE CROSS-LEGGED POSITION

The closeness of this position makes for truly sensual sex. He sits on the floor with his legs crossed, then she hops on top with her legs around his waist and her arms around his back. Now, in Tantric style (see page 42), both lovers close their eyes, breathe in time and concentrate on drawing energy through their bodies. If Tantra isn't your style, just enjoy this position for the swooning intimacy it brings and take the opportunity to kiss and caress your way to the peak of arousal.

SUPER-SESSION

Keep going for hours – she can up the intimacy and eroticism with some energetic squat thrusts to keep him nice and hard. If he wants to rest at any point, he simply lies back and watches her in action – a guaranteed turn-on.

kiss
& caress

ELEVENTH POSTURE

You'll be completely wrapped up in each other in the
Eleventh Posture, which demands yoga-like flexibility
from the woman. She lies on a pile of cushions with the
soles of her feet pressed together and her knees out to
the sides. Then her lover lies on top. If this is more than
her groin or thigh muscles can take, there's an easier
version, shown here, in which he penetrates first then
she presses her soles together behind him.

BREAST CARESS

Guys: you're ideally poised
to pay some attention to
her breasts in this position.
Kiss and nuzzle the sides
(an area that often gets
neglected) before you take
her nipple in your mouth.

be entwined

THE CLASPING POSITION

This position is great for that "I'm so in love with you" feeling. You can't get any closer. It's also good for an intimate reunion after a physical – or emotional – separation. It lends itself to soulful partings, too. Don't hold back: he can clasp her head in his hands, you can push your bodies together, wrap your arms around each other in a bear hug. Breathe, sigh, pant, moan. Tell each other what you feel. If he's got a strong erection, he can lie still inside her while she "milks" him by squeezing her love muscles (see pages 52–53).

soulful sex

SIDEWAYS SEX

The *Kama Sutra* also recommends the side-by-side clasping position, which is just a roll away. Hold each other tight and go for it. Then if you want to, just roll back again.

SENSUAL PLEASURE • MELTING MASSAGE

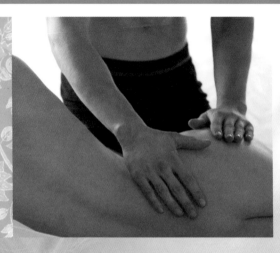

Prepare for some sensual lovemaking with an erotic massage – as well as getting you both nicely aroused, it's the perfect antidote to the stresses of a long, hard day. Sex may be the last thing on your lover's mind at the beginning of the massage, but it won't be by the end …

WHAT YOU NEED

This massage uses a simple stroking technique. You don't need any special equipment – just some towels (warm from the radiator) and some massage oil. You can buy ready-made massage oil or you can make your own by adding 20 drops of a relaxing essential oil, such as lavender, to 50ml (2fl oz) of a carrier oil, such as almond oil. Alternatively, just grab a bottle of olive oil from the kitchen cupboard and you're ready to go.

WHAT TO DO

Step 1: Start with a head massage. Ask your partner to sit in a chair, then stand behind them and place the heels of your hands on their temples and your fingertips on the crown. Hold their head like this for a few moments and ask them to close their eyes and relax by breathing deeply. Slowly move your hands in large, slow circles. Now rake your fingertips through your lover's hair and make gentle shampooing movements all over their scalp.

Step 2: Once you've melted some tension, help your lover to undress and lie face down on the bed on top of some warm towels. Join them by stripping off, too – it makes things intimate and sensual rather than clinical. Pour a little massage oil into your cupped hands and rub them together to warm the oil. Kneel behind your lover's head and let your oiled palms glide down the length of the back. At the buttocks move your hands apart and draw them slowly but firmly back up the sides of your lover's body. Keep repeating this stroke. Ask for simple feedback such as "softer" or "harder".

Step 3: Re-oil your hands and then straddle your lover's thighs. Draw a firm line along either side of their spine using your index and middle fingers. Pause at the shoulder muscles to press your fingertips in circular movements. Repeat as many times as you like.

Step 4: Still straddling your lover's thighs, let your fingertips move in random swirly patterns all over their back. Make your touch light and feathery and keep re-oiling your hands so that your fingers glide smoothly. Finally, gently lower your body so that your entire front covers their back (guys: take some weight on your elbows if you're in danger of crushing her). Kiss and nuzzle the back of their neck and whisper an invitation to turn over when they're ready

When the massage is over, ask for feedback to find out what your lover most enjoyed. Then lie together and savour the intimacy of the moment, before making love if you wish.

SENSUAL PLEASURE • KEEP ON KISSING

Kissing well is an act of profound sensual communion. The most memorable kisses are those you get lost in. You just can't think of anything you'd rather be doing, anywhere you'd rather be, or anyone you'd rather be with. Peak kissing experiences – like peak experiences of any kind – are difficult to pre-arrange. However, what you can do is make sure that, if the situation presents itself, you're at optimum kissability.

• Make sure you taste good. This goes without saying, but a flossed, minty mouth is always nicer to explore than a stale one. No matter how much you're in love, how long you've been together or how forgiving your partner is, be devout about oral hygiene.

• Start soft and slow, and build up. Brush your lips against your lover's. Briefly enclose one of their lips in yours. Be flirty and tentative and wait for your moves to be reciprocated rather than going in all tongues blazing. The exception to this is when you're both so turned on that neither of you can hold back.

• Heighten the intensity of a kiss by touching your lover with your hands. Be tender rather than out-and-out sexual. Cup their face in your hands, gently stroke their earlobes or run your fingertips softly down their back.

KISSING – WHY WE DO IT

According to studies, the first kiss a couple exchanges can make or break the relationship. It's not all down to technique either – when you kiss someone you receive valuable information about their health, genetics and hormonal status via pheromones and other chemicals present in saliva. In biological terms, it's a way of finding out whether you and your kissing partner are well matched as potential mates. You might not pull away from a snog thinking "I can't reproduce with you because you're genetically incompatible," but you might have the sense that a person doesn't taste or smell "right" to you. Or, on the simplest level, they don't turn you on. So if you find yourself unmoved by a kiss, don't blame yourself or the person you're kissing – just put it down to biology. When you do find that connection with someone through kissing, make the most of it.

KISSING KAMA SUTRA STYLE

Vatsyayana's advice on kissing is complicated by contemporary standards. There are different kisses for different occasions and even different regions. A virgin may kiss by placing her lips upon her lover's lips (the casual kiss), by making her lower lip throb against her lover's lip (the throbbing kiss) or by brushing his mouth with the tip of her tongue (the brushing kiss), while her hand is placed over her lover's eyes.

Other types of kissing include "the bowl" in which one partner rubs their tongue over the teeth, palate and tongue of the other; "lip drinking" in which the lips are pressed together and the tip of the tongue is used; and "the stirring kiss" which is used by a woman to arouse a man who is sleepy or distracted. The key for modern-day lovers is to vary your kisses.

CICADA ON A BOUGH

Sex from behind can be sensual, as this position proves. Imagine a cicada perching on a branch – he's the cicada; she's the branch – and you'll get the gist of this sex position from the Tao. It's at the romantic end of the spectrum of rear-entry poses. If you don't like the raw animalism of the doggie position, but want deep penetration and the eroticism of belly against buttock, this is perfect. The position of the heads means lovers get to whisper to each other and he can use his spare hand to gently trace the shape of her lips or make feather-light strokes along her jaw-line ... delicious.

talk dirty

DEEP LOVEMAKING

If you like extra-deep-penetration, place pillows beneath her to push her bottom up. Guys: start with slow, shallow thrusts, then increase your speed and depth slowly. The Tao recommends 54 thrusts, – but don't get hung up on counting.

THE BOW POSITION

Although your bodies are far apart in this position, there are still plenty of opportunities for intimate and sensual caresses. The woman lies on her back with a cushion or pillow underneath her bottom, which raises the so-called "seat of pleasure". This allows for deep, satisfying, precision penetration. Even if you feel silly arranging the cushions at exactly the right height for comfort, you'll be glad later when you're moving in perfect rhythmic harmony. The Bow Position is also exhilarating for her because she's slightly inverted. He, meanwhile, gets to act the dominant part and be in control.

PLEASURE HER

Unlike many a man on top position, the front of her body is exposed which makes it easy for both him and her to caress her nipples or slip a hand between her legs. There's even enough room for her to slip a vibrator against her clitoris – especially one of the pebble-shaped ones that fit neatly in the palm.

CICADA TO THE SIDE

A more intimate version of "spoons", this position lets you see each other's faces. Compared to its sister position, Cicada on a Bough (see pages 20–21), it's romantic rather than raunchy, and sedate rather than frantic – both of which are great for slowing things down and focusing on the nuances of sensuality. If you want to up the raunch-factor, she can raise her leg in the air.

THE FINAL TWIST

When you want to go deeper and faster, just twist or roll into Cicada on a Bough (see pages 20–21) and he'll be able to move to his heart's content.

take it
nice *&* slowly

TRY TANTRA • A SENSUAL SPACE

Stimulate all your senses and create true sexual intimacy by making your bedroom a haven of pleasure – a place where you can both fully relax and concentrate on satisfying each other in comfort and without distractions. In Tantric-style sex, preparing your bedroom for lovemaking is an essential part of the ritual.

A BEAUTIFUL BEDROOM

Picture walking into a yoga class with piles of laundry on the floor, a mobile phone bleeping in the corner, and a stale smell in the air. Chances are you wouldn't be able to fully relax. It's the same with Tantra – you need to feel totally connected and completely relaxed in the place where you're practising.

So before you begin any Tantrice exercise, take a look at your bedroom. If it's messy or cluttered, take action. Get rid of anything that distracts you, anything electronic that buzzes, rings or bleeps, and any unfragrant smells. When you've finished, ask yourself whether your space appeals to each one of your senses. If it doesn't, how can you enhance it? You don't have to set up an elaborate Tantric altar or splash out on new silk bed linen. The following are easy ways to change a room from functional to sensual:

  Place vases of fragrant flowers in the room (if you can't get fresh flowers, burn an essential oil such as jasmine in an essential oil burner).
• Play some music very quietly in the background. It should be so quiet that you can hear yourself (and your partner) breathe above the volume.

Choose something that doesn't have distracting lyrics – perhaps something classical, a chant or a recording of waves lapping against a shore.

- Make the bed the inviting centrepiece of the room: think soft, fluffy pillows and cushions, and clean, fragrant sheets (sprinkle a few drops of your favourite essential oil on them). Keep any thing you might need, such as massage oils and towels, no more than a small arm-stretch away.

- Turn your heating on if there's any danger of getting cold. You need to be able to sit and lie around naked without getting goosebumps (at least not the "it's-freezing-in-here" type).

MIND SEX • SEDUCING THE MIND

What can be more intimate than getting inside your lover's mind ... Great sex is not only about pleasuring your lover's body – getting them in the right frame of mind can make a huge difference to both their and your enjoyment of a sexual experience. Planting a sexy thought can be a faster track to arousal than an hour of foreplay. For example, you and your partner might be lazily watching television or getting ready for work ... sex couldn't be further from your mind. Then your partner utters a few magic words and suddenly you've got to have each other. The trick is to know the words that will flick that sexual switch in your partner's brain.

TAKE THEM BY SURPRISE

One of the biggest passion killers in the bedroom is routine. Anything that's repetitive gets boring and this even applies to the way you talk to your lover. If you habitually talk dirty, it tends to lose its power to thrill. If you're shy or coy, the novelty of the "how-can-I-lure-her-into-bed" chase eventually wears off. Vary your approach – if you're not the type to be direct or explicit, whisper "I want to ∗∗∗ you now." Or if romance isn't your usual style, use phrases like "making love" – it may sound corny to your ears but your lover will enjoy the novelty of a new approach.

USE COMPLIMENTS

A genuine compliment is often a more seductive gift than any amount of roses, candlelit dinners or bottles of champagne. Being complimented can make you feel properly sexy – it can make you walk taller, dress more daringly, and act more confidently both in and out of bed. There's an art to paying a compliment:

- Make it specific. Instead of "those jeans look nice," say: "I love your bum in those tight jeans."
- Make it sexual: instead of "I really wanted to wake you up when I got home last night," say: "I really wanted to wake you up and ravish you when I got home last night."
- Mean what you say. Look your lover in the eye as you compliment them.
- Be sparing. One really sweet and genuine compliment is worth a dozen throwaway ones.

IF YOU CAN'T SAY IT, WRITE IT

If you're the tongue-tied type, technology can come to your aid. Use text, chat or email to convey a sexy message to your lover. What better way to brighten their day and begin to get them aroused for coming home to you in the evening. Even if you can say what you feel, a written message has a unique power to thrill (and the recipient gets to keep it, too). The shared secret between the two of you is a great way to add to the intimacy.

But don't always rely on technology. The old-fashioned approach works well and in some ways can be more romantic – an erotic handwritten note that is hidden in your lover's bag or placed on their pillow at night, containing a dirty request or a declaration of your love, can make them tingle with anticipation.

THE TWINING POSITION

In this position, you truly melt into each other. The *Kama Sutra* says the woman should place one of her calves across the back of her lover's thigh. By doing so she draws him in to her. She can also use leg pressure to control his thrusting. Clamping her leg tightly around him means "stay still in me and let's savour the moment", whereas pounding his hamstrings with her heel means "don't stop that rhythm."

HOT LOVEMAKING

This is a great position to take each other to climax in front of a roaring fire on a cosy winter night.

draw him in

PRESSING POSITION

This is the extra-intimate, sex-meets-hug version of the missionary position. He climbs on top and she wraps him up in her arms and legs. Or for more ambitious lovers, he picks her up in a standing position (see page 121), carries her to the bed and lays her down. Reserve this option for grand romantic gestures as it's more stimulating to the emotions than the genitals.

TOTAL HARMONY

Breathing in time in this position is a good way to get connected to each other. See pages 142–143 for more about getting close to each other through breathing.

THE FIRST POSTURE

This may be a missionary position, but in terms of sexiness, satisfaction and intimacy it's an out and out winner – you get to see each other's faces, hold each other and move freely. Even though he's on top, it doesn't mean that she has to lie passively below. She can undulate so that her hips rise to meet him on every thrust. Guys: you can respond by being creative with your moves. Do lots of fast shallow thrusts in a press-up position, then take her by surprise by sinking deeply into her, holding her in your arms and grinding rather than thrusting.

SLOW IT DOWN

The sexy comfort of The First Posture makes it easy for men to race their way to orgasm. If you want to delay ejaculation, reach down and gently tug your balls away from your body.

thrust
together

CONTRARY POSITION

Flesh on flesh ... in this *Ananga Ranga* position the woman is instructed to "apply her breast to the man's bosom" as she lies "straight upon his outstretched body". He then takes her waist or buttocks firmly in hand and moves her accordingly. There is added intimacy as she doesn't have much leverage to move because her legs are parallel with his.

TIGHT FIT

Try to concentrate on the friction produced by the close fit between your geni-tals – especially the way the base of his penis is tightly pressed to her clitoris.

naked bliss

KAMA SUTRA WISDOM • SEX MOVES FOR HER

You can add your own sensuality to your love-making by the way you move on top of your man. Vatsyayana says "A man can learn everything about a woman from the way she moves when she's in charge." Here are some sexy *Kama Sutra* moves for the girls. She gets to control the depth and pace while he lies back and enjoys …

THE TONGS

Pull him deeply inside you and hold him there. Squeeze your pelvic floor muscles as hard as you can (see pages 52–53) – as though you're trying to grip him like a pair of tongs. Relax and contract your muscles if you need to. When you feel like moving your body, gently gyrate your hips.

THE SPINNING TOP

This position is more for novelty than intense sensation and, as the *Kama Sutra* wisely notes: "it can be done only with practice." He lies on his back and she straddles him in a sitting position, so you're both face to face. Once you've assumed the position, she twists around "like a wheel on an axle" so she's facing his feet. As she twists, he thrusts to keep things erotically charged (and himself erect). See if you can feel any novel sensations. Even if you can't, congratulate yourself on pulling off a tricky centuries-old manoeuvre!

PLAYING THE PART OF THE MAN

A woman may also "play the part of the man" and try using some of the sex strokes for men (see pages 34–35). For example, he can lie on his back while she kneels astride him with her hands on either side of his head — now she rapidly bobs up and down by rhythmically flicking her hips. This is the female version of frolicking like a sparrow (see page 34). Churning is a good orgasm-inducing stroke because it stimulates the clitoris, — she sits on top of him and grinds her pelvis in circles or back and forth (see page 34).

Here's Vatsyayana on the subject: "When the man has tired himself by continuous movement but still wants to carry on, the woman may help him by playing the man's part himself. She can also play the man's part out of her own desire or to stimulate the man's erotic imagination. When a man and a woman take turns at leading, they can make love continually without interrupting the flow. She can say 'You threw me down and now I am throwing you down!'"

DOMINATE HIM

It's great for him when she takes the lead and gets on top. Not only does it take the performance pressure off him, it offers him the chance to watch her wriggle and writhe — one of the biggest male turn-ons. Watching is educational as well as titillating (guys: note the pace, rhythm and movements she chooses when you're lying still). Plus, if he usually ejaculates quickly, this can slow things down and delay his climax — not because her taking charge is any less erotic, but because it stops him from moving in the fast in-out way that usually guarantees him an orgasm. So, girls, don't be shy about taking the lead.

KAMA SUTRA WISDOM • SEX MOVES FOR HIM

The *Kama Sutra* understood the subtler details of sex and, as a man, you can add warmth and generosity to your lovemaking by how you move inside your woman. The standard in-and-out movement of the penis works for most people but the following strokes give extra variety. Some of them are especially good for women because they give more sustained attention to the clitoris – which sometimes gets neglected by the in-and-out thrusting movement.

CHURNING

There are two variations of churning: in the first the man takes hold of his shaft and "churns" it on her clitoral area. The direct friction of his glans on her most sensitive bits is incredibly stimulating. Do it until you're both near orgasm and then penetrate and thrust. The second variation involves him penetrating deeply and then moving or churning his hips so that his shaft massages every bit of her vagina.

THE DAGGER

The less daunting name for this stroke is the "piercing movement". His pelvis is above hers when he enters her. This helps to position his shaft against her clitoral hood and head. As he thrusts, he aims to press the front of her vagina and reach the very top on each stroke.

GRINDING DOWN

This is the opposite of the dagger. He's still on top but the woman raises her hips and the man makes only shallow strokes, aiming to penetrate just the outer part of her vagina (this is the site of a woman's "most extensive itch" according to the *Kama Sutra* – and also the opinion of contemporary sexperts and scientists).

PRESSING

In the pressing position, he sinks into her as far as he possibly can and stays there (hence "pressing"). He should imagine that he's trying to get the very root of his penis inside her (but should go lightly if he's on the big side). This is great for slowing things down, tempering extreme arousal and sharing a tender mid-sex cuddle.

THE BLAST OF WIND

This titillating move is performed during mid-sex. He pulls out of her as far as he can without withdrawing completely, hovers for a few tantalizing moments and then plunges back in hard and fast.

THE BOAR'S THRUST AND THE BULL'S THRUST

To practise the boar's thrust, he simply enters her as normal but then thrusts so that his penis rubs against one side of her vagina; to practise the bull's thrust, his penis should rub each side of her vagina alternately.

FROLICKING LIKE A SPARROW

Approaching the point of no return? This is the stroke to use. He moves in and out rapidly while keeping most of his penis inside her.

skin to skin

FISH

This position is the ultimate in sensual treats. She starts by giving him a foot massage and then slowly works her way up his body using herself as a massage tool – she uses her lips, tongue, fingers, breasts and even her hair to tease and tantalize him and build his sense of anticipation. Finally, when her genitals are parallel with his, she sinks on to him, slowly enclosing the length of his shaft (if he hasn't got an erection by this point, she should head down again). Now she moves her hips in slow voluptuous circles.

GIVE YOURSELF

Making your lover the focus of your attention can be blissful. In this position, devote yourself to the act of giving. Imagine you can feel the sensations you are delivering to your lover in your own body. Express your pleasure vocally.

THIGH CLASP

The Thigh Clasp rates highly for gazing into each other's eyes, kissing and neck nuzzling. Girls: get him in between your thighs and don't let go. This is a great position for tightly packed intensity and, for some women, it's got great orgasm potential. Instead of thrusting, both lovers grind their pelvises together, rocking against each other (when she rocks forward he rocks back, and vice versa).

HOT MOVES

He can move his upper body away from hers so that you're in a wide V-shape – this changes the angle of entry and stimulates different erotic zones for both of you.

don't let go

POSITION OF INDRANI

This position ticks lots of boxes: intimacy, romance, passion, eye contact, deep penetration, skin-to-skin contact ... Like many *Kama Sutra* sex positions, it's a man-on-top position and, because her legs are pressed to her chest, he alone is in charge of the motion. If you enjoy the feelings of dominance and surrender that this brings, go for it. Then, if you want, switch round so that she has a turn to go on top and take charge.

delve deep

MOVE WITH CARE

Position of Indrani allows deep penetration, so care is called for. Because his penis can pound her cervix in this position, he should start with slow gentle strokes. When she's at the peak of arousal the upper part of her vagina expands or "balloons" and she can take more of him in.

MIND SEX • FLIGHTS OF FANTASY

The closer you and your lover are, the easier you'll find it to share your sexual fantasies. Used in the right way, they can enhance sexual pleasure for both of you Fantasizing is the low-risk way of testing your sexual boundaries and experimenting with the naughty, the dirty and the taboo. So if you've ever fancied a threesome, an orgy or joining the mile-high club with a stranger, what are you waiting for? Fantasizing is also a great way to add an extra frisson to sex with your lover or solo masturbation. If you're in the mood for sex but your body isn't keeping up, an erotic fantasy can make you erect or wet in half the time.

FANTASY FODDER

Maybe you've already got a huge and colourful collection of fantasies (plus numerous back catalogues). But what if you haven't? How do you become a fantasizer (assuming you want to)?

The answer is to steep yourself in sexy stuff – books, films, websites – and get carried away (there are worse ways to spend a weekend indoors!). You don't necessarily have to go in a hard-core direction – start off by "exposing yourself" to erotic films such as (9½ Weeks or Sex, Lies and Videotape) and books such as Nancy Friday's My Secret Garden. Read about other people's fantasies on the internet. Buy a kinky novel and read it at bedtime.

Although some people have obscure fantasies and fetishes, the majority of us are turned on by similar sorts of things: anything that pushes us a bit beyond the sexual mainstream (although what

people define as "mainstream" can vary from missionary position sex for one person to bondage for another). Sometimes even revisiting a sexy encounter from your past has the power to turn you on – if so, re-live it. Visualize the most titillating bits in glorious, colourful slow motion. Embellish and improve on reality. No one will ever know.

TO SHARE OR NOT TO SHARE

Let common sense prevail when deciding whether or not to reveal your fantasy. If you get a drug-like high from imagining sex with your gorgeous/recent/super-successful ex, it's probably best to work that one through on your own. If however, you're fantasizing about something that could add a whole new frisson to sex with your lover, then go ahead. If you feel shy about sharing, ask your partner to do a fantasy swap: you reveal one, they reveal one. Try to keep an open mind when listening to your partner's fantasy, even if it isn't an immediate turn-on for you.

EXPLORE TOGETHER

If you don't like face-to-face revelations, invite your lover to have a sexy web surfing session with you – take turns to search for whatever you want to on a sex-related theme. Treat it as a game – but use it as an opportunity to reveal and discover what turns you on. And if you end up on the floor under your computer desk wrapping each other's bits in cling film, so much the better.

TRY TANTRA • SEX BREATHING

One of the great things about Tantra is that it gives you an immediate way of slowing down sex, so that it's more sensual, more connected and more sexy than the usual fall-into-bed-at-the-end-of-the-day sex. A good way to do this is through controlled breathing.

CALM AND CONNECT

Start by undressing and sitting opposite each other. You can sit on the bed or on the floor, cross-legged. When you feel settled, close your eyes and bring your attention to your breath. Follow its path through your nostrils and see where it ends. Make a conscious effort to pull your breath deeply down, so that your belly swells outward (put your hand on it and feel the movement). Imagine you're inhaling your favourite fragrance and you want to draw it as deep inside your body as you can.

Get absorbed in observing your breath. Release any tension from your muscles. In particular, check that your jaw, shoulders and belly aren't clenched or contracted. When you feel you're relaxed and in a rhythm, open your eyes and look at your partner. Wait for them to meet your gaze and then slowly start to sense each other's breath. Listen to its sound. Observe its rhythm. If you're close enough to each other, feel it on your cheek. Now start to breathe in time together. The idea is to connect to your partner through your breath — forget your surroundings and everything that's going on in your life. All that matters is the present moment.

THINK SEXY

Hold your partner's gaze and focus on sexy or loving feelings you have for each other – how much you fancy them/love a particular feature of their face/like the way they smell. Keep breathing in sync with each other. The more you practise this exercise, the easier it gets. If you keep doing it for long enough without talking, giggling or pouncing on each other, you'll get a sense of melting into each other. Ultimately you'll start feeling as though you don't know where you end and your lover begins. Follow this by cuddling each other, then see what happens next.

really make love

SOULMATES SEQUENCE

Try this deeply intimate sequence, from left to right, for sex with lots of cuddling and skin-to-skin contact. Starting in a woman-on-top position – Fish – at first she's in control of the movement. (Girls: if woman-on-top positions are your orgasm trigger, exploit this one to the full – he's on top for the rest of the sequence.) Next cling tightly to each other and roll 180 degrees so that he ends up lying above her in the missionary position (the First Posture), staying joined throughout the movement. He moves closer into her in the Pressing Position and she wraps her legs tightly around his waist. For the finale, she brings her knees up to her chest and he gets on his hands and knees in the Position of Indrani.

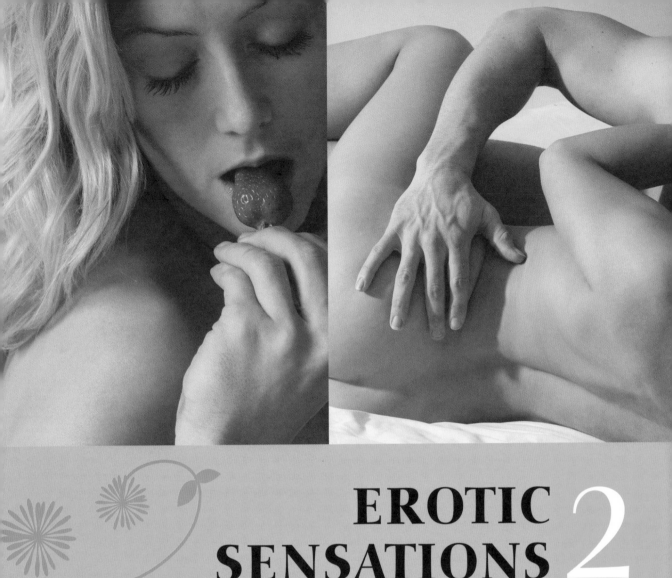

EROTIC 2
SENSATIONS

take
her
now

FANTASY LAND

Like all rear-entry poses, the Elephant is ideal for giving yourself up to a fantasy. If you're short of inspiration, turn to pages 40–41.

ELEPHANT

It's dirty, it's anonymous and it's highly recommended for those moments when she wants to chill and he's in the mood for a raunchy work-out. Elephant is a slinky and seductive sex position that will feel fantastic. He'll love the raw animalism of thrusting from behind; she'll love lying flat and focusing on the pressure that's mounting on her G-spot (see pages 72–73). Guys: get into position, and do slow then fast push-ups.

15

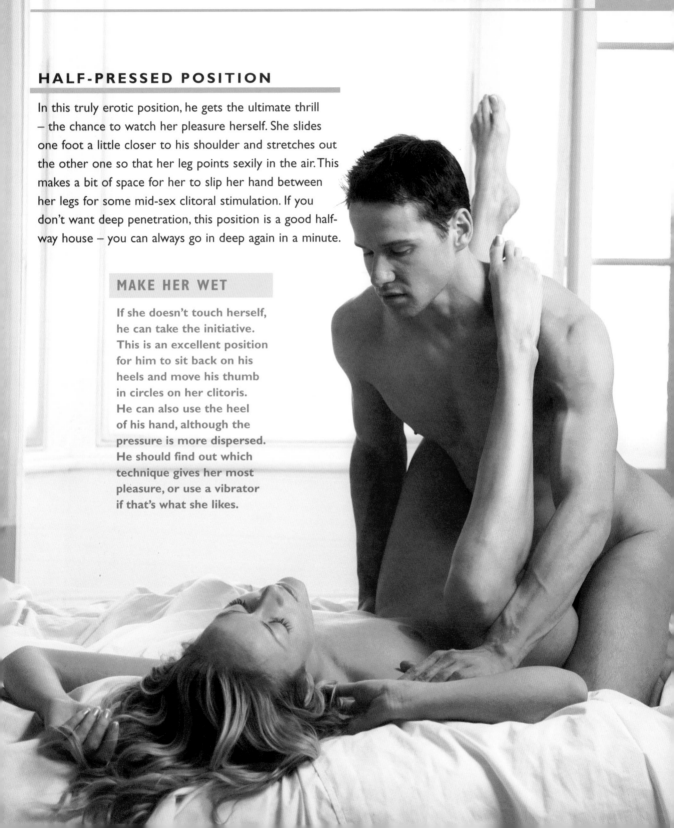

HALF-PRESSED POSITION

In this truly erotic position, he gets the ultimate thrill
– the chance to watch her pleasure herself. She slides
one foot a little closer to his shoulder and stretches out
the other one so that her leg points sexily in the air. This
makes a bit of space for her to slip her hand between
her legs for some mid-sex clitoral stimulation. If you
don't want deep penetration, this position is a good half-
way house – you can always go in deep again in a minute.

MAKE HER WET

If she doesn't touch herself,
he can take the initiative.
This is an excellent position
for him to sit back on his
heels and move his thumb
in circles on her clitoris.
He can also use the heel
of his hand, although the
pressure is more dispersed.
He should find out which
technique gives her most
pleasure, or use a vibrator
if that's what she likes.

SILKWORM SPINNING A COCOON

In the highly arousing Silkworm Spinning a Cocoon, he's on top but she's in control. The woman wraps her legs around her man in a super-sexy embrace that tells him exactly how much she wants him. She can jerk her hips back and forth while he stays still. And if she wants a rest, he can take over in a more conventional missionary position. She can also send an erotic charge through him by running her hands up and down his thighs.

thrill him

COCOONED IN SEX

Lose yourself in this erotic workout for two. If you start to think about anything other than the sex you're having, pick a part of your body and concentrate on it. It could be your penis or clitoris or another hot spot, such as your nipples.

TRY TANTRA • LOVE MUSCLE WORK-OUT

It's so erotic to imagine that your lover might be doing this love muscle work-out secretly beneath their clothes. The exercises can be done without visibly moving a muscle, anywhere: on a busy train, in a business meeting, while sunbathing or even on a date. Both women and men can do them and they're an integral part of Tantric sex practice.

The point of Tantric sex is to channel sexual energy up a "tube" that runs from your perineum to the crown of your head (known as the inner flute – see pages 88–89 – or the hollow bamboo). This is a sophisticated practice that takes time to master, but the important techniques you need to learn are: chakra breathing (see pages 88–89), pelvic rocking (see pages 64–65), and good old-fashioned pelvic floor exercises, known in Tantric circles as love muscle exercises.

WHERE ARE THE LOVE MUSCLES?

Love muscles, more technically known as pelvic floor or pubococcygeal (PC) muscles, sit at the bottom of your pelvis. They control the opening and closing of the vagina, urethra and anus. You can locate them right now by imagining that you're bursting for a pee but trying to hold on – the muscles that you contract to do this are your PC muscles.

HOW TO EXERCISE

Having located your love muscles, contract and release them rapidly. Do this repeatedly for about a minute. On each contraction draw your

muscles up to their full "height", and on each relaxation, let them go completely. Now start to breathe in time with the movements – contract your muscles as you inhale and relax them as you exhale. Do this for a further two minutes. Be selective about which muscles you contract – all your movements should be internal. So, for example, if you're pulling your tummy in on each contraction, make a conscious effort not to.

Now you can move on to the next stage of the exercise – this is harder in that you need to hold the muscle contractions for longer than just a split second. As you inhale, pull up your love muscles and hold them (and your breath) for a count of five to 10 seconds. Then release them fully (imagine you are trying to urinate). Keep doing this for five minutes. Practise both stages of this exercise once a day.

THE REWARDS

Like many aspects of Tantric sex, it can take time to master and benefit from the techniques. You probably won't be able to channel sexual energy up your inner flute straight away – although synchronizing your breath with your muscle movements is an important first step. But there are some wonderful sexual benefits that you'll notice soon after you start exercising your love muscles. He will have strong erections (because these exercises encourage blood flow to his penis), and she will develop excellent vaginal muscle tone. She'll be able to grip him more tightly during sex and experience more intense sexual sensations.

MIND SEX • THE ART OF UNDRESSING

If you want to tickle your partner's mind with a truly erotic gift, undress for them. Put on some sexy music, dim the lights and start swaying your hips. And if you're thinking "oh, that's just for brazen exhibitionists", read on …

Two of the most common deterrents from stripping are "I wouldn't know where to start" or "my body isn't sexy enough". To tackle the former, watch a strip scene in a film and shamelessly copy the moves. Or search for stripping on the internet and find a routine that works for you. Then practise. Watch yourself strip in front of a mirror. Pretend you're 16. Once you've learned the routine start throwing in your own moves and flourishes. Even if you decide never to perform in front of your partner, enjoy yourself.

BE CONFIDENT

If you haven't got a perfect body, rest assured that a good strip is 99 percent attitude. See it as an opportunity to show off your sexual power. Be bold, confident and at home in your body (whatever its size or shape). If shyness takes hold, pretend you're on your own and you're doing this entirely for your own titillation. Move in ways that feel comfortable and sexy. Your aim is to please – yourself.

If your confidence is still flagging, use tricks to boost it. Strip by candlelight rather than strip light! Choose undies that flatter your body shape. Position a mirror behind you – this not only gives your audience a back view but also allows you to turn round and perform to yourself.

STRIPPING TIPS

- Don't wear tops that you have to pull over your head – choose something that can be tantalizingly unzipped or unbuttoned.
- Keep moving all the time you're not undressing. All your moves should come from your hips: wiggle, rock, undulate, thrust.
- Enjoy it and look like you're enjoying it. Go slow as if you've all the time in the world.
- Tease your lover – reveal something and then conceal it again.
- As each bit of clothing comes off, throw it at your lover.
- Keep your hands busy throughout the routine – if they're not shimmying a shirt over your shoulders or slowly snaking a belt away from your waist, put them on your hips or in the air with your wrists crossed.
- Give your audience a variety of angles – turn your back from time to time. Throw a backward glance over your shoulder.
- Girls: make the unveiling of your legs a key part of the show. Put one foot on a chair as you unzip killer high-heel boots. Now slowly unroll that stocking down your thigh.
- Guys: wear a T-shirt under a shirt to give you more to take off. Keep your pelvis moving as you strip. Whirl your clothes above your head. Wear a hat so she can't always see your eyes.
- Once you're down to your undies, caress your skin, glide your hands over your hips, run your index finger just inside your underwear. This should satisfy your audience!

HORSE SHAKES FEET

Having some distance in lovemaking can add to the eroticism and make you want each other even more. In this position she keeps him apart from her with one leg on his chest and the other one on his shoulder. The restraining influence of her feet gives him the chance to thrust lightly in the outer part of her vagina. This is the most erotically charged zone and has great orgasm-making potential, especially when he combines shallow thrusting with a finger or two on her clitoris.

orgasm heaven

NIPPLE PLAY

If he has sensitive nipples, her foot is perfectly placed for some nipple caressing and tweaking. For a smooth sensation, she should rub oil into his chest and on to her toes beforehand.

EIGHTH POSTURE

Packed with erotic pleasure, the joy of the Eighth Posture is in the fact that the woman's legs are pressed together. This makes everything feel much tighter – more tightness means more friction, which means more intense sensation. Some women find it easier to come when their legs are together – because the pressure feels more concentrated on their clitoris. The Eighth Posture works best when he's well endowed and can still penetrate her easily despite the fact that her thighs are almost closed. If he's not well endowed, he can use his hand to twirl the head of his penis on her clitoris or he can do some pre-sex thrusting between her thighs.

tight &
tantalizing

MAKE IT SLIPPERY

Any sex that involves a tight fit can be helped by a dollop of lube. When his bits slip easily against hers, it makes positions like the Eighth Posture a lot more viable – whatever his size.

KAMA SUTRA WISDOM • MOUTH CONGRESS FOR HIM

You can create some truly erotic sensations with your mouth and "mouth congress" was something that Vatsyayana had a strong opinion about. He described eight techniques to be performed one after the other in strict succession including "sucking a mango fruit" and "swallowing up". After each technique, the giver was instructed to "express a wish to stop". She should only carry on when implored to by her lover. Whether you like to give a blow job that's formulaic or free-style, here are some *Kama Sutra*-inspired moves.

THE NOMINAL CONGRESS

Warm him up slowly by kissing and nuzzling his penis with your lips – keep your tongue firmly inside your mouth at this stage. Gently place the tip of his penis between your lips, then kiss him along the length of his shaft. Keep everything slow and seductive. You're not trying to make him come yet – you're just saying a very sexy hello.

BITING THE SIDES

Although Vatsyayana uses the word "biting", most men will feel more comfortable with "nibbling" or "grazing". You need to get him wet, so coat his shaft in lube (choose one that's designed to be licked) or use your tongue to "paint" him with saliva. When he's slick, take his penis in hand and approach side on – open your mouth wide and enclose a portion of his shaft. Very gently press with your teeth. Now let your teeth glide softly over the surface until your mouth is closed. Keep doing this until you've covered his whole penis.

PRESSING THE OUTSIDE

You're moving past the warm-up stage: take the head of his penis in your mouth and gently suck. Swirl your tongue around his frenulum, then softly draw your lips over his glans. Repeat.

PRESSING THE INSIDE

The same stroke as the last one but this time take more of him in your mouth – take your lips as far down his shaft as is comfortable.

KISSING

Hold the bottom of his shaft in your hand and kiss his head and shaft. "Kiss" means plenty of wet and swirling tongue movements. At the same time, move your hand up and down his shaft.

RUBBING

As before, but take your lips out of the action and concentrate on rubbing, licking and flicking with your tongue. Keep a steady rhythm.

SUCKING A MANGO FRUIT

Go for the climax with both your hand and mouth working in rhythmic harmony. Your hand pumps the bottom and middle of his shaft. The top of his shaft and his glans plunges into your mouth. Suck on each plunge.

SWALLOWING UP

Carry on what you're doing but move your mouth further down so that he feels like he's being "swallowed up". Prepare for ejaculation!

KAMA SUTRA WISDOM • MOUTH CONGRESS FOR HER

Delve deep into her with this erotic foreplay session. The *Kama Sutra* advised that "the way of kissing the yoni should be known from the way of kissing the mouth". It's a good starting point, but, fortunately, we now know much more about female anatomy than the sexperts of Vatsyayana's era. And, often, knowing precisely where to put your tongue is the best guarantee of truly sensational orgasmic lip service.

OPENING MOVES

Rather than diving straight in, spend some time building up sensation in the local area – gently kiss her belly, pubic mound and the insides of her thighs. Caress her with your breath. Go slowly like you've got all the time in the world and, if the mood takes you, moan appreciatively. If she knows you're happy there, she'll be happy too.

GETTING HOTTER

Now it's time for Vatsyayana's advice: he says you should kiss her between the legs like you'd kiss her on the mouth. Make your tongue soft and exploratory and don't zone into any particular area yet. Swirl your tongue along the length of her vulva – aim to get the whole area wet and slick, if it isn't already. Try taking her labia in your mouth and gently sucking.

AND HOTTER

When you know she's aroused (be aware of the subtle changes, such as a change in her breathing, as well as the more dramatic ones, such as

moaning or thrusting her hips), start to pay specific attention to the area around her clitoris. Make your tongue into a point and circle it around her clitoral hood, gradually getting faster (but not to a speed that you can't sustain). As things hot up, move your attention to her clitoral head – the little bud just under the hood. Move your tongue and lips across it either in circles, side-to-side movements or simply back or forth. You can also gently suck her clitoris – keep your tongue moving on the head as you hold it in your mouth. Tip: if your tongue gets tired, give it a break by substituting your fingers for a while.

CLIMACTIC MOVES

As in orgasmic massage (see pages 136–139), pace and rhythm are key in bringing her to a climax. If she likes what you're doing, keep doing it and be prepared to stay exactly where you are until she comes (unless this is pre-sex foreplay and she's urging you to get on top). Keep your lips and tongue moving rhythmically on her clitoris but give her vagina some attention, too.

By inserting one or more fingers into her vaginal entrance, you'll be stimulating the nerve endings in this sensitive area – either move your fingers in and out, starting shallowly at first and then going deeper, or press your fingertips on her G-spot (see pages 72–73). During her climax keep your stimulation going right until her final orgasmic contraction has ended. But take your cues from her – if she pulls away from you, you should pull away, too.

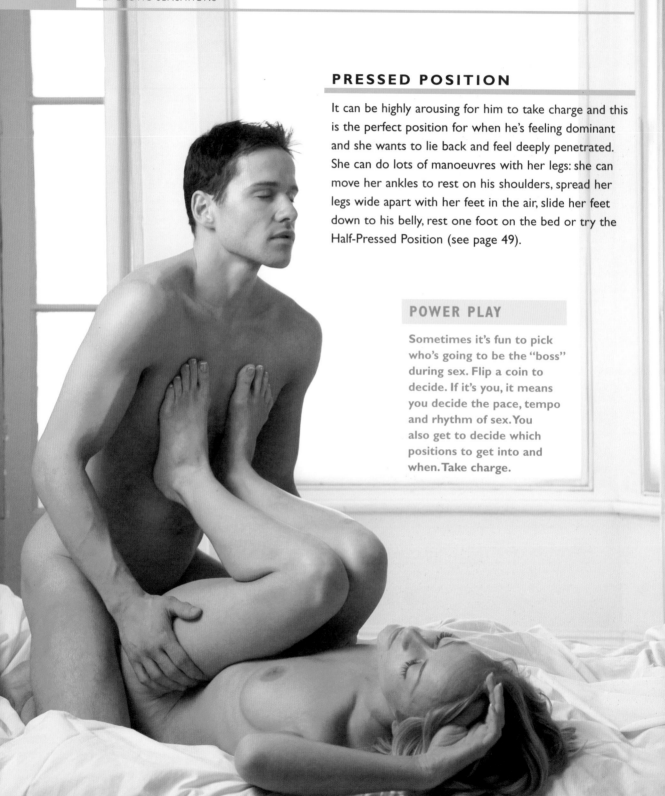

PRESSED POSITION

It can be highly arousing for him to take charge and this is the perfect position for when he's feeling dominant and she wants to lie back and feel deeply penetrated. She can do lots of manoeuvres with her legs: she can move her ankles to rest on his shoulders, spread her legs wide apart with her feet in the air, slide her feet down to his belly, rest one foot on the bed or try the Half-Pressed Position (see page 49).

POWER PLAY

Sometimes it's fun to pick who's going to be the "boss" during sex. Flip a coin to decide. If it's you, it means you decide the pace, tempo and rhythm of sex. You also get to decide which positions to get into and when. Take charge.

LARGE BEE

If he enjoys an erotic wake-up call, this is the way to
do it. She uses her hands or mouth to coax his penis
into action, then leans over him and plants featherlight
kisses from his neck down to his belly and then along
the length of his shaft. She then straddles him in a squat
(think of a hovering bee about to suck nectar and you'll
get the point of this position). He doesn't take much of
her weight but still gets the joy of being tightly enclosed
by her. She can move back or forth on him (or do squat
thrusts if she wants an early morning workout).

FUN FOR ALL

In this position, she gets to
control the pace and the
rhythm and how deeply
he penetrates. He relin-
quishes the control he has
over movement but gets to
watch her at her sexiest.

TRY TANTRA • THE ROCKING HORSE

Tapping into your sexual energy makes for some highly erotic sexual sensations. This exercise builds up sexual energy in your pelvis, which prepares you for some of the more complicated Tantric practices. But, apart from anything else, it presses all your erotic buttons and feels great.

ROCK SOLO
Practise this on your own at first. Being alone helps you to focus inward and concentrate on all the delicious sensations building up inside you.

Get a pillow and put it under your buttocks and tuck your heels underneath. Your spine should be straight, your feet parallel, and your hands should rest in your lap. Check you're not holding any tension – scan your belly, shoulders and jaw. Shrug your shoulders a few times or massage your jaw with your fingers to relax these places. Relax your stomach muscles.

Now move your pelvis back and forth in a rocking motion (pretend you're on a rocking horse). To get the right movement imagine there's a string pulling on your pubic bone on the forward rock and a string pulling on your tailbone on the backward rock. Focus on the feelings in your genitals as you rock – if you find it a turn on, enjoy it. Let the arousal build – it's the whole point of the exercise, so give yourself up to it.

SYNCHRONIZE YOUR BREATHING
When you've got used to the rocking movement synchronize your breathing with the rocking – breathe in on the backward movement and

breathe out on the forward movement. Do this for a few minutes to get a natural rhythm going. Now slow things down. Rock your pelvis into the back position and hold your breath for a count of 10. Then slowly exhale as you push your pelvis forward. Keep doing this.

As you rock and breathe, imagine that the air you inhale is going deep into your body – all the way down to your genitals. Let the air tickle and stimulate your clitoris and vagina or your penis and balls. Keep rocking and breathing. Let all your thoughts go – just focus on the delicious rhythm of movement and breath. If you practise this technique everyday, you'll notice that all the good sensations start to merge into one. Your whole pelvis – not just your genitals – will be alive and tingling with sexual energy.

ROCK WITH YOU

If you and your lover have practised the Rocking Horse individually and know you can successfully get into an erotic rhythm of breath and movement, try doing it together. Kneel facing each other and start off separately with your eyes closed. When you've established your rhythms, open your eyes and look at each other. Gradually synchronize your breath and movements – as her pelvis moves forward so does his. As he exhales so does she. As she holds her breath so does he. Feel a sense of connection that goes beyond the everyday. If you feel silly or have the urge to laugh, reserve those feelings for later. For now, just be playful and see what happens …

MIND SEX • BE A TEASE

Up the eroticism of your lovemaking with some tantalizing tease techniques. One of the seductive things about a lover you barely know is the "Will they? Won't they?" tension. Will she kiss me? Will he come home with me? Will she have sex with me? When the answer turns out to be "yes" the rush can be drug-like. So what do you do when you've been together for years and there is no uncertainty about ending up in bed together? The answer is: you tease and seduce anyway.

If your partner is a sure-thing, you won't need to compete with other people to get them into bed. However you'll almost certainly have a new set of rivals: your partner's work or day-to-day domestic chores or even the television. These things can distract your lover from following you into the bedroom. So rise to the challenge and get teasing. Think dirty rather than clean. As the *Kama Sutra* says: lovers are allowed to talk suggestively of things normally considered coarse.

FIND NEW TERRITORY

Take sex out of the bedroom – surprise your lover as they're getting out of the bath and offer to dry them. Pay attention to their naughty bits. As always, the art of teasing consists of giving a little and holding back a little – as soon as they become aroused take your towel to a lesser erogenous zone. Then home in again. Leave them in doubt about your next move. Choose other venues to play tease: the kitchen, the dining room, or even the garden, so long as you're not over-looked by inquisitive neighbours.

DRESS UP

Staying in for the night? Swap comfy clothes for sexy ones. Wear indoors what you consider too risqué to wear outdoors. Alternatively, just wear underwear – buy something sexy and let your partner discover it by asking them to undress you. Impose a look-but-don't-touch rule at first.

ARRANGE A TRYST

Call it a tryst or call it a dirty weekend – spend some time apart and then meet your lover in a hotel bar at an appointed hour. Even if you can't manage the whole strangers-getting-to-know-each-other role-play, ban any conversations that are mundane, work- or money-related, or that bring up gripes or stresses. The benefit of a new location is that you get to act like new people.

PARTY FOR TWO

Stay in and party. The three essential ingredients are wine, music and dancing. Plan the music in advance. Choose your favourite sexy, seductive and sentimental tracks. Dance close, dance apart and take turns to dance for each other. End by stripping for each other (see pages 54–55).

GO ON A SEX DIET

Agree on a short period of sexual abstinence. The rules are: you can touch each other in any way you like – licking, kissing, stroking and massaging are fine. But no sexual penetration is allowed. You'll quickly find original ways to tease and please each other and enjoy experimenting!

SIXTH POSTURE

For sheer eroticism and burning arousal, this can't be beaten. AKA the doggie position – the Sixth Posture was practised in 16th-century Tunis and it's still a classic today. He gets the visual stimulation of her bum curves, plus he can watch his penis slide in and out. He also gets to dominate and have no-holds barred thrusting power. Meanwhile she gets the submissive joy of feeling "taken" and deeply penetrated by him. One of the few drawbacks if she's on the floor is friction burns, so she should kneel on something soft.

G-SPOT PLEASURE

It's tempting for him to thump hard and deep in this position, but if he can slow down a little he can give her some sensations to die for. If he can picture where her G-spot is (see pages 72–73), he can aim the head of his penis towards it. Move slowly and carefully – precision targeting is your aim – and press rather than thrust against her front vaginal wall. Repeat as necessary!

down & dirty

SEAGULLS ON THE WING

Guys: this is your chance to arouse and indulge your lover in some spine-tingling sensations. Ask her to sit on the edge of the bed and lie back and close her eyes. Pick one of her feet up and gently kiss the sole. Now work your way up her calf and her thigh, and apply your tongue to her clitoris. Do this for a really long time. When you're pretty sure that you can't arouse her any more without tipping her over the edge, get into a kneeling position, hold her firmly with your hands and enter her.

on the edge

EASY ENTRY

The exhilarating thing about sex in this position is the way the penis is parallel to the vagina – it normally enters at an angle, so this will feel novel for both of you. If he finds he's not quite high enough for comfort, he can kneel on some pillows.

SENSUAL PLEASURE • HIS SWEET SPOTS

Your partner has erogenous zones and hot spots – but he also has explode-in-ecstasy spots. If you can locate and stimulate them, you'll secure a safe place in your partner's affections.

THE P-SPOT

One of the most sensitive spots for him is the P-spot, sometimes known as the male G-spot. Stimulating it when he's aroused can boost sexual intensity, heighten sensation and bring him to a powerful climax. The P in P-spot stands for prostate – a gland that plays an important role in ejaculation. It produces the fluid that makes up semen and contracts to produce ripples of pleasure when he comes. You can't touch the prostate gland directly because, unlike most of his sensitive bits, it's hidden inside his body. (It's underneath his bladder and above his perineum.) The good news is that you can access it remotely via two routes – route A is through his anus and rectum, and route B is through his perineum.

Route A: If you take route A you'll need one or two fingers and plenty of lubricant. Girls: if he's new to P-spot stimulation, ask him to lie on his back, then kneel between his legs. Lavish him with some oral attention first then stroke the area between his balls and anus, gradually zoning in on the anus. (By the way, the anus is rich with nerves and is another one of the spots that will make him giddy with pleasure – so pause here to stroke, press and circle with your fingertips.) Gently push one or two generously lubricated fingers inside him and press your fingers against his front wall (in the direction of his belly). Firmly rub and stroke the area with your fingertips – search for a spot that stands out from the surrounding tissue or just "feels different". Ask him if he likes static pressure or movement. If you can, stimulate his penis at the same time – the more aroused he becomes the firmer and more distinct his P-spot will feel beneath your fingers. Press harder as he approaches climax, but always take your cues from him – verbal or non-verbal.

Route B: If you opt to take route B, simply press firmly upward on his perineum with your fingers – ask him for direction about the exact spot to press. Clue: it's nearer to his anus than it is to his balls. Even though route B means you're further away from his actual prostate gland (making the sensations less intense), it's an easier technique to use during intercourse or oral sex. Plus if you, he, or both of you are squeamish about anything to do with anal play, which many people are, you're still one step removed.

THE F-SPOT

If you prefer to stick to front-end stimulation, explore the F-spot instead. F stands for frenulum – it's the delicate tissue that lies on the underside of his penis just below his glans. You can heighten the pleasure of oral sex (see pages 58–59) or a hand job (see pages 138–139) by lavishing lots of attention on this spot. Press your thumbs into it or swirl and flick your tongue across it.

SENSUAL PLEASURE • HER SWEET SPOTS

If you want to hit the erotic epicentre of a woman's body, then you have to know what's going on behind the scenes. The clitoris, for example, is largely hidden. You're bound to have heard of the G-spot, but have you heard of the A-spot and the U-spot? Here's a road map of what's where – and what to do when you get there.

THE CLITORIS

The little head that peeks out of the clitoral hood is just the tip – behind the scenes the head is connected to a shaft that splits into two legs (think of a wishbone on a chicken) that run in a backward direction past her urethra and vagina. When she becomes aroused the entire clitoris fills up with blood and gets erect, just like his penis. So stimulating the internal bits of her clitoris as well will turn her to putty in your hands.

An excellent way of tackling both the internal and the external clit is to stimulate her hood and head while also moving your fingers in and out of her vagina – your fingers will be massaging her clitoral legs as they pass the vagina. As her clitoral legs become more engorged and erect, her vaginal entrance will tighten around your fingers. Experiment with different ways of moving your fingers and stay near the entrance as this is where she's most sensitive.

THE G-SPOT

Now press your fingertips against the front wall of her vagina (the wall on the side nearest her belly), and introduce yourself to her G-spot. It's about 5cm (2in) up and feels different from the surrounding area – ridged and oval in shape. Not all women like G-spot stimulation but for those who do it can turn a good orgasm into a mind-blowing one. Press firmly into her G-spot and try massaging it in circles. Or ask her which she prefers – movement or static pressure. Mix G-spot stimulation with clitoral attention – use all the tools at your disposal, your fingers, your tongue or a sex toy designed to target the G-spot or vibrate against the clit. When she comes, keep that firm pressure on her G-spot – don't release it until after the final ripple.

THE A-SPOT

Slide your fingers further up the front wall of her vagina and you'll come across her A-spot. Like the G-spot, it's full of nerve endings, and when massaged can help some women to orgasm (especially if combined with G-spot stimulation). Play "find the A-spot" with her lying on her back and you between her legs. Ask her to close her eyes as you give her a fingertip massage of her front vaginal wall until she says "Yes!"

THE U-SPOT

This spot is around her urethral opening where she pees from. Try touching it in the way you'd touch her clitoral hood – circling and rubbing with your fingertips. It's so close to the clitoris it gets neglected or gets "overlap stimulation" rather than receiving the dedicated attention that will ensure she enjoys some new sensations.

FOURTH POSTURE

From intimate to erotic in one move – a sexy way to get into this position is for her to sit astride him while he kneels on the bed so they're in a face-to-face cuddling position. After they've kissed and cuddled their way to a body-tingling high, she lowers herself back on to the bed (keeping her bum closely snuggled into his groin) and then raises her ankles to hook them over his shoulders.

DRESS THE PART

Girls: if you like dressing for sex, this is your chance to show off sexy stockings or a pair of high heels. Make the Fourth Posture your gift to him at the end of an erotic dance or striptease (see pages 54–55).

surrender
to him

NINTH POSTURE

This erotic pose has got the raunchiness of the doggie position but without being so dirty and animalistic. Do it instead of the doggie position when you want that extra bit of intimacy or when you don't want poundingly deep penetration. Take up your positions by the side of a bed or sofa. To experiment, position yourself near to a mirror and get a kick out of the voyeurism.

I WANT YOU NOW

Make this one of the sex positions you use for spur-of-the-moment, got-to-have-you-now sex. If there's no bed handy, she can always hang on to a bath top, a table or press her palms flat against a nearby wall for support. You can also do it at the bottom of the stairs.

uninhibited

FIFTH POSTURE

There's something friendly yet oh-so-erotic about
sideways sex. Perhaps it's because neither of you can
dominate. Or because it's like a naughtier version of the
missionary position. Get close to each other and find
a rhythm that feels good – give each other plenty of
"mmmms" and "ohhhhhs" as feedback. And, once you've
found that rhythm, don't stop. And take advantage of
being face to face – kiss, whisper and gaze at each other.

SLOW RHYTHMS

Sideways sex can delay his
climax. This is because he
can't move quite as freely.
So, guys, if you're worried
about coming too soon,
guide your lover into the
Fifth Posture and take the
slower, scenic route to
orgasm. She doesn't even
have to know why.

erotic
rhythm

BAMBOO

Pick this position for a fast erotic charge. It works best if she's taller than him and he's well endowed. But it can be adapted – guys, if you're finding it hard to make your entrance, squat down and ask her to part her legs and lean back. Or she can gain some height by wearing heels (not when you're doing it in the shower though). Even if he only enters her a little way there's a good chance the head of his penis will land on her G-spot (see pages 72–73). The other option is for him to thrust between her thighs without actually penetrating. If you're both equally aroused, the parallel friction between the top of his shaft and her vulva will make your legs tremble (a good excuse to fall on the floor and carry on).

make it quick

WANDERING HANDS

Do wonderful things to your lover with your hands. Cup her breasts in your palms and circle her nipples with your thumbs. Press your hands on his hips or buttocks and pull him into you.

turn up the heat

RED-HOT SEQUENCE

Try this sequence, from left to right, in which he takes the dominant role, while she stays wide open and receptive. He starts by kneeling upright. She places her left foot on his chest and her right foot over his shoulder in Horse Shakes Feet. Then, she slides her left foot up over his shoulder, so that both her ankles brush his ears in the Fourth Posture. Next, she brings her right foot down to his chest in the Half-pressed Position. To get into the Pressed Position, which offers the deepest penetration so far, she puts both her feet on his chest near his collar bones. All these positions are variations on a theme — but you'll discover that every change of leg position produces a stimulating new angle or sensation.

PURE
PLEASURE **3**

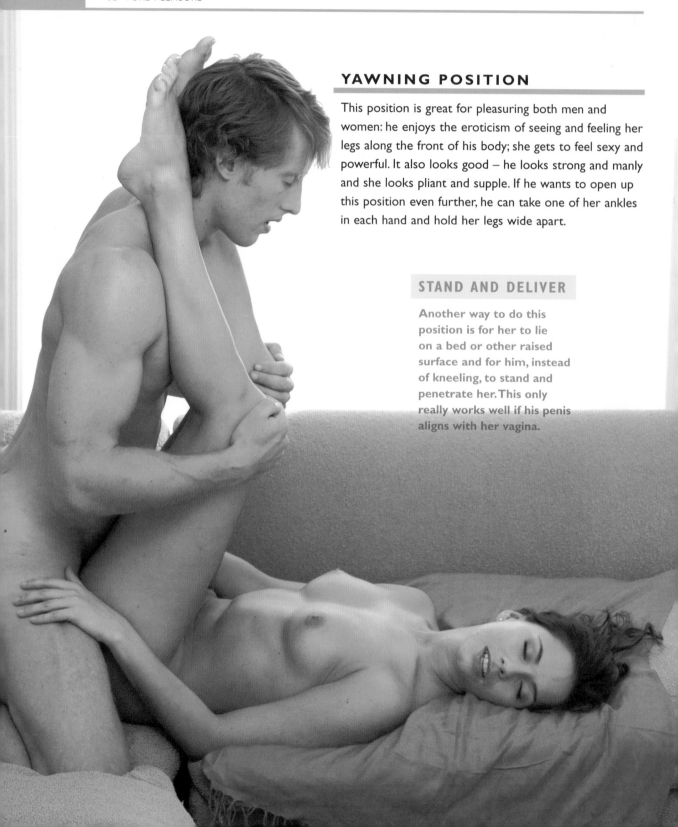

YAWNING POSITION

This position is great for pleasuring both men and women: he enjoys the eroticism of seeing and feeling her legs along the front of his body; she gets to feel sexy and powerful. It also looks good – he looks strong and manly and she looks pliant and supple. If he wants to open up this position even further, he can take one of her ankles in each hand and hold her legs wide apart.

STAND AND DELIVER

Another way to do this position is for her to lie on a bed or other raised surface and for him, instead of kneeling, to stand and penetrate her. This only really works well if his penis aligns with her vagina.

RIDING THE MEMBER

Looking for some new thrills? Try this. He gets into a knee-to-chest pose while lying on his back. Then he puts his erect penis between his legs so that his glans points towards the ceiling. Meanwhile, she straddles him and guides as much of his shaft into her vagina as she can (if you want deep penetration, don't choose this position). Now she bobs up and down. Riding the Member hits the spot for men who want to explore their vulnerable side and women who want to be in the driving seat. She can reach behind and caress his balls. He can cup her buttocks in his hands and guide her movements.

THE THRONE

A variation of Riding the Member is the slightly more difficult The Throne. He draws his knees close to his chest and keeps his calves at right angles to his body. The backs of his thighs form the seat of the throne and the backs of his calves form the back of the throne. Now she simply takes her seat with her back to him.

GALLOPING HORSE

This one is for kinky pleasure – even though there aren't any cuffs or restraints being used, it feels like he's holding her down. Guys: imagine you're on a bolting horse. Grab her ankle with one hand and the back of her neck with the other (no pressure on the front of the neck though). Now hang on as you thrust, pump and grind your way to the peak of arousal. Try it if you want to know what it feels like to be dominant or to be dominated.

take
charge

PLEASURE PLAY

If you want to try out more kinkiness, invest in some cuffs, paddles and restraints from a sex toy shop. Turn to page 86 for some tips on how to deliver a skin-tingling spank during sex.

KAMA SUTRA WISDOM · MODES OF STRIKING

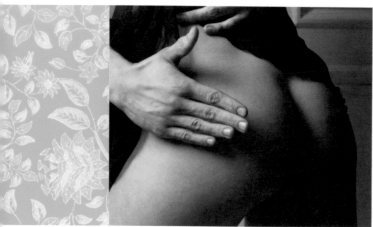

While many people don't equate pleasure and pain, the *Kama Sutra* compares sex to a quarrel in which, at the height of passion, it's acceptable to lash out at or strike your partner. By modern sexual standards, this would be considered violent – and at best a practice for self-proclaimed sadists. However, this doesn't mean you can't use a modified version and indulge in light spanking.

If you want to try a bit of kinky sex play, spanking is a fun and non-threatening way to start (providing you're both willing). It's also a light-hearted way to build up trust and intimacy. You can make spanking your main sexual event or you can deliver a few well-aimed spanks during sex for instant titillation.

Most sex positions lend themselves to him spanking her rather than the other way round. Any woman-on-top position in which she straddles him, either facing his head or his feet, is ideal for a mid-sex spank. So, too, is any variation of the doggy position. It's possible for her to spank him in a side-by-side position, but she'll have easier access if she spanks him prior to sex – girls: get him to lie flat on his front or, for true kinkiness, get on all fours or bend over.

SPANKING TIPS

- Remember your aim is to deliver a light and tantalizing sting – not pain. If it doesn't feel good, stop. Remove rings beforehand!
- Massage your partner's bottom (see pages 94–95) to get things off to a relaxed start.
- Unless you're aiming for sudden shock value

(and you know your partner gets off on this), start gently. Cup your hand and let it land lightly on your partner's bum. Gradually increase the speed and force of your swing.

- Up the kink-factor by alternating the stinging sensation of a spank with the sensual relaxation of stroking and rubbing.
- Get your aim right – avoid bony areas, such as the bottom of the spine or the tail bone. Your target is the muscular or fleshy cheek. If he's slapping her, he can aim low on her bum so the feeling vibrates through her genitals. She should steer clear of his genitals, most notably his balls.
- If your recipient has had enough, stop straight away and give them a cuddle – and a loving kiss on the bottom.

SPANKING TOYS

- If you and your partner love spanking, buy a paddle from an online sex shop. They come in all shapes and sizes and they're usually made of leather or rubber. Some have shapes cut out of them so you can brand your lover's bum with a row of hearts or kisses, for example. Others have a soft furry side and a hard leather side so you can alternate pleasure and pain.
- Another prop is the spank tie, a piece of flexible wire encased in soft rubber – you use it to bind your lover's ankles or wrists so they can't escape, although if you play any kind of bondage game, decide on a "code word" in advance (see page 134) in case you want to stop.

TRY TANTRA • THE INNER FLUTE

In Tantric sex, pleasure and fulfilment come from harnessing the sexual energy that is released during an orgasm and keeping it inside the body. To do this, you channel that energy up your "inner flute", a "pathway" that runs from the genitals to the crown of the head. Along this pathway are seven energy centres, or chakras, which yield different pleasurable sensations.

THE CHAKRAS

The first chakra: This base chakra lies along the inner flute between the anus and genitals. When you channel energy through your base chakra, you feel physically and emotionally secure.

The second chakra: The sacral chakra below the navel governs sexual pleasure. Energy flow through this chakra makes you feel full of vitality.

The third chakra: The third chakra is the solar plexus chakra, just below the ribcage. You will experience the flow of energy through this chakra as a sense of personal power and courage.

The fourth chakra: The heart chakra, the centre of love compassion, is the fourth chakra. It lies in the centre of your chest. When sexual energy rises through it, you'll feel a sense of connection and merging with your lover.

The fifth chakra: The fifth chakra is in the hollow of your throat. As energy flows through it, you'll be able to express yourself openly.

The sixth chakra: The sixth chakra is the forehead chakra, which is the centre of intuition and imagination. It lies on your forehead between your eyes. Insight and honesty come as energy rises through this chakra.

The seventh chakra: The seventh chakra is the crown chakra on the top of the head. When your sexual energy rises to this point, you feel a blissful sense of union with everything and everyone – this is the ultimate aim of Tantric practice.

WHAT TO EXPECT

If you commit to Tantric sex on a regular basis, you'll be rewarded with feelings of physical pleasure that vibrate throughout your body. If you need an incentive, imagine an orgasm, not only in your genitals, but everywhere. You also feel a sense of bliss, oneness and connection with your partner and with everything around you.

Just because the fruits of Tantric practice don't appear overnight, don't be discouraged. From the very first time you do an exercise with your partner, you'll feel like you're connecting in a new way, particularly if your usual sexual style is fast and orgasm-centric. Tantric practice is all about preparing your space (see pages 24–25), slowing things down and appreciating subtle aspects of bodily sensation. If you've never looked into your lover's eyes for more than a minute, breathed together or felt the tingling of arousal anywhere other than in your genitals, do the Try Tantra exercises throughout this book.

hold on tight

THE CHEAT'S VERSION

If you can't master this
one on land, do it in water.
Suddenly, she'll be as light
as a feather. It will feel
deliciously sensual. Your only
challenge is to find a swim-
ming pool where you have
guaranteed privacy.

SUSPENDED CONGRESS

This adventurous position can make for truly thrilling
and certainly memorable sex. It's a fun one to try outdoors when you wouldn't be able to lie down anyway
– think pine forest or deserted car park. Girls: you can
help out in this position by wrapping your arms tightly
around him and pushing off against the wall (or tree)
with your feet. Even if neither of you are relaxed enough
to come, you'll experience a satisfying thrill.

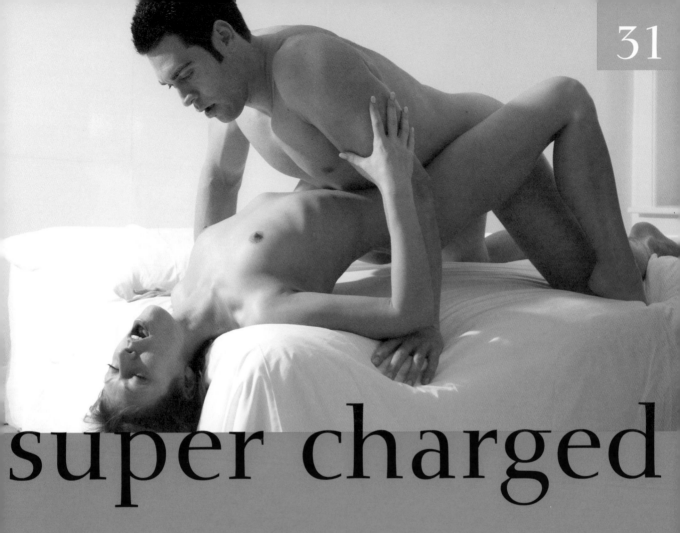

super charged

WIDELY-OPENED POSITION

The satisfaction comes from the fact that you can both reach orgasm in this position. She opens herself as widely as possible to him and moves her body up to meet his. He feels not just embraced, but completely desired. If she's strong, he doesn't have to move at all; she just raises and lowers herself on his penis (keeping her bum off the ground). To make the most of this position, she should move as slowly as possible, aiming to feel every inch of his shaft. On each downward movement, she contracts her vaginal muscles tightly to "milk" him.

LASTING PLEASURE

Draw the experience out. Play around with it. Get near to the point of no return and then pull back. Hover on the brink of orgasm for as long as you can. Make sure you let each other know what you're doing; and when you can't last any longer, say so.

SPLITTING OF A BAMBOO

To find new pleasure zones, it helps to be experimental. She starts with both legs over his shoulders as he leans in towards her. Then, she drops one leg so that her foot is flat on the bed. Next, she switches leg positions so that her lower leg now rests on his shoulder. She keeps doing this for as long as he stays in the position, and gets a great leg workout too!

thrill me

SAY WHAT YOU WANT

Don't be afraid to ask your lover to do more of a sexual technique, or move position slightly if it enhances your pleasure. They will want to please you, but can only do so if they know exactly what you want.

SENSUAL PLEASURE • EROTIC MASSAGE

It's all too easy to forget how to really touch each other, yet it can be so pleasurable. Erotic massage brings passion, playfulness, as well as a new connection, eroticism and sensuality to your lovemaking. This erotic massage targets three major erogenous zones (the bottom, chest and toes) and gets you and your lover into a steamier mood. You might want to start with the massage techniques on pages 16–17 and afterwards continue with genital massage (see pages 136–139).

WHAT TO DO

Step 1: Give your lover a big sexy hug from behind, slide down their body and sit astride their thighs, just below bum level. Smooth some oil into their buttocks using firm pressure. Rather than just pressing down with your arms, lean your body weight into your hands. You can twist your knuckles or the heels of your hands into the buttock or you can knead the muscles between your fingers and thumbs.

Step 2: If you're into spanking (see pages 86–87), now's the perfect time – the sting and the surprise will be an instant eroticizer. If you're new to spanking, cup your hand slightly, relax your wrist and aim for the muscly centre of the buttock. Follow the spank with soft, soothing strokes with the palm of your hand. As well as your hands, use other parts of your body to massage the buttocks – long hair and shaved heads create tickles and tingles of pleasure. Kisses, nibbles and bites feel good too. Girls: rub oil into your chest and slide up and down on him so your breasts rub against his bum.

Step 3: Help your lover to roll over (tell them to stay relaxed and floppy). Kneel at their head and reach your hands down on to their chest. If you're massaging a woman, keep your hands flat and move them in slow, sensual circles around her breasts. Then place your palms on the sides of her breasts – slowly push them up so that your index and middle fingers form a V around her nipples. Bring your index and middle fingers together to pinch her nipples and then lift your hands away. Keep repeating this stroke.

If you're massaging a man, stroke the whole of his torso with light feathery strokes, and then massage his chest using the flats of your hands (fingers splayed). Glide your hands down the centre of his chest, then part them and pull them up the sides of his body. If your man is a fan of nipple caresses or kisses, include this in your massage too, but not all men like this.

Step 4: Move down to your lover's feet (cover the rest of their body with warm towels). Gently take one foot in your lap. Squeeze it along its length and kiss the sole. Stroke oil into the skin using firm circular thumb pressure all over the surface. Now slowly push your index finger in and out between each of your lover's toes – this feels undeniably sexual. Then take their toes in your mouth and nibble and suck them – as though you're giving a mini blow-job.

MIND SEX • PUTTING ON A SHOW

Sexual exhibitionism is about being proud of your sexual power and showing it off for both your and your partner's enjoyment. If you like dressing up and performing, sex is a natural area in which to indulge your exhibitionism – your audience may not be large but they will certainly be attentive. And, even if you aren't a born extrovert, there's no harm in slipping into a sexy costume and seeing where the mood takes you …

SEXHIBITIONISM

Your performance could be a striptease (see pages 54–55), a dirty dance or an outrageously kinky costume. But you can also sprinkle exhibitionistic acts into daily life with your partner to keep their eyes – and thoughts – firmly on you.

Girls: bend over in front of your partner to pick something up (so what if you forgot to wear pants under that short skirt?). Bend from your hips so your bum stays high in the air – keep one knee slightly bent – and don't be in a rush to stand up again. Guys: shave or trim your body hair (pubes included) and strike a pose naked on the bed ready for when she walks in the room. Girls: wear something naughty and unexpected (nipple clamps/a basque/body paint/high heels and nothing else) and straddle him while he's watching television. Guys: serve her breakfast in bed wearing a pair of latex shorts – and don't forget the rose between your teeth!

If none of this seems quite you, try on some costumes before you reject the idea of dressing up and parading yourself. Find a look that fits

your personality. Bear in mind that kinky, sexy or theatrical clothes have an amazing ability to transform the wearer and push you into new ways of behaving. Somehow a wig, fetish gear and a whip will compel you to act like a dominatrix even if you're usually prim and conservative.

FILM STAR

Another favourite exhibitionist activity is to film yourselves while having sex. If you don't like commercial porn, it's great to have your own personal footage to get aroused to. It's easy to do – you just need a digital movie camera and a tripod – but the challenge is to produce something that looks good. For the best results:

- Shoot some footage and watch it back – if something's not working, you'll quickly know not to repeat it.
- The most unflattering angle to shoot from is below – if you're hand-holding the camera, always point it down or across rather than up.
- Don't feel you have to play the part of a porn star – simple arousal and shared passion can be far more erotic.
- Connect your digital movie camera to the television so you get live feedback.
- If you want to look slimmer, choose standing or lying positions rather than sitting ones. Arching your back and stretching your arms over your head are other tricks of the trade.
- Choose flattering lighting, such as uplights or candles – using harsh overhead lights will emphasize your imperfections.

PACKED POSITION

This is a fantastic leg trembler – him because of the intensely packed sensations on his penis; her because of the position of her legs combined with the genital-melting feeling. The fact that her legs are close together (and crossed) makes penetration feel tauter and tighter, and increases friction. If she's super-supple, he can lean against her legs and push them closer to her body – this way there is deep and tight penetration. But this may only be possible if she's been to yoga classes recently.

TIE ME UP

Want to try some light bondage? He ties her ankles together with a scarf, then she props her feet against his shoulders.

locked tight

KAMA'S WHEEL

The closeness of this position will bring you both pleasure. She sits astride him, stretches out her legs, holds on to him for support and leans back. She shouldn't make sudden movements as his penis is at an unusual angle. A slow lean backward may guide his penis to her G-spot (see pages 72–73). Neither of you will be able to move much – adding to the intimacy – but try flexing your love muscles (see pages 52–53) and concentrating on the small sensations rather than the big ones.

CLIMB HIM

Girls: add a titillating twist to this position by leaning back on your elbows and raising first one and then the other leg slowly and seductively on to your lover's shoulders. Hold his gaze while you do it.

SENSUAL PLEASURE • THE 69 POSITION

The 69 position is all about mutual pleasure – and what greater thrill for you and your lover than to come together through sensational oral sex. In the 69 position, in which you give each other oral sex simultaneously, the sheer thrill of being so close to each other's genitals at the same time is highly erotic and arousing.

The 69 position isn't a modern invention – people were doing it in Vatsyayana's time. As he said: "Sometimes a man and a woman may turn so they lie head to foot and make love to each other with their mouths – this is Congress of a Crow."

THE SENSUAL SIDE OF 69

A 69 doesn't only have to happen in moments of high passion and naughty excitement; there's no reason why it shouldn't also be a slow, sensual act. Instead of going for a high-maintenance position such as her straddling his face or him straddling hers, lie side by side and head to toe in a relaxed way. The merits of this position are: both of you can get comfortable; it's "equal" in that neither one of you feels over-exposed (or smothered); and it's easier than other positions to adjust if you're different heights.

Once you're in position, rather than heading straight for his penis/her clitoris, take a leisurely approach that consists of some thigh stroking and nuzzling. Give each other's pubic triangle some attention – tweak their pubes if they've got any; tickle or nibble their skin if they haven't. Reach around and lightly scratch their buttocks. Even when your tongue eventually arrives on your lover's hot spot, try to keep your mouth movements playful and light at first before hotting things up a little.

A common criticism of 69 is that it's difficult to come because you're both so busy trying to service each other. There are two simple solutions. Either strike orgasm off your "to-do" list. (After all, you can always let it happen later in a position that's more conducive to lying back and letting go.) Or decide that you'll take it in turns to be the dominant giver. So, for example, while she is lavishing his penis with lots of fast rhythmic mouth movement, he could be taking a backseat by giving her the occasional crotch kiss or tongue flick. Even if he just buries his head in her thighs and moans, she'll still be receiving some localized pleasure.

BESPOKE SEX

Like any sex position, 69 should be tailored to your bodies and your sexual tastes and needs. If you find a finger potentially more orgasmic than a tongue, then use 69 as a manual sex position or manual/oral combined; if you like your oral sex served with G-spot stimulation, then use a sex toy that's specially designed for the purpose; if you enjoy anal stimulation, bring that into the mix, too. In short, forget about 69 being a route to fast, dramatic, simultaneous orgasms. Instead, think of it as a handy position from which to look at and explore each other's most intimate parts – whether with your mouth, fingers or a favourite sex toy.

KAMA SUTRA WISDOM • BITES AND NIBBLES

Given in the right way, a bite or nibble can add passion and pleasure to lovemaking. In Vatsayayana's time, biting was seen as a sign of high passion. Bites were something to look at and smile upon – a sign of sexual ownership. There were different bites for different sites.

THE BITES OF LOVE

The Hidden Bite: Lower lip – recognizable by excessive redness of the skin.

The Swollen Bite: Cheek – same as the Hidden Bite, but with more force and pressure.

The Point: Lower lip – a bit of skin is nipped between two teeth to create a point on the skin.

The Line of Points: Thighs – the skin is nipped between two teeth to create a line of points.

The Coral and the Jewel: Cheek – a bite that involves bringing the teeth (the jewel) and the lips (the coral) together until a mark is left.

The Line of Jewels: Neck or thighs – the same as the Coral and the Jewel but repeated in a line.

The Broken Cloud: Top of the breasts – a circle-shaped bite.

The Biting of the Boar: Top of the breasts – reserved for moments of great passion, this is rows of teeth marks with red patches between.

FOR TODAY'S LOVERS

Whereas lovers in the time of the *Kama Sutra* bit each other to make their mark or demonstrate passionate abandon, today's lovers are more likely to bite because it feels sensual for the recipient. Good nibbling and biting sites include the earlobes, the bum cheeks, the back, the shoulders and the thighs. Always check that your lover is happy to be bitten. Most people don't want to be marked, but if you do want to create a purple blotch on your lover's skin, the quickest way is to suck rather than bite. The harder you suck, the more livid the mark.

APE

This brings deep pleasure. She rolls back as if going into a shoulder stand and he grabs her hips and penetrates her. Or she can hook her legs over his shoulders while he's kneeling back on his heels and then he raises her up with his hands under her bum. This position allows for deep penetration so she should be thoroughly lubricated beforehand. Try warming up with some of the more intimate, less athletic positions in chapter 1.

deep thrust

A TIGHTER FIT

The Ape is an ideal position for what the *Kama Sutra* would describe as a low sexual union – when she has a long vagina and he has a short penis. When she brings her legs towards her chest, her vagina contracts and maximizes feeling for both lovers.

hard
& fast

RISING POSITION

She parts her legs in a wide V-shape. He climbs on top.
The result is a sexy take on the missionary position. It's
ideal for those moments when you're overcome with
lust and don't want anything too experimental or fancy.
This isn't a position for slow, gentle moves – now's
the time for thrusting genital-bumping. Get breathless.
Writhe. Make as much noise as you want to: moan,
pant, gasp, cry, scream. Let go.

JUST FOR VARIETY

Two ways to add variety:
she grabs hold of her ankles
with her hands and pulls
them towards her head
(only for the very supple).
Or he penetrates her from
a standing, kneeling or
squatting position from the
side of the bed while holding
her ankles wide apart.

37

ANKLE BRACE

This is different and fun! He traps her feet or ankles
in his grasp and she traps his. Now you're both equally
stuck, you've got to figure out how to move. This is the
fun bit – you're forced into coming up with creative
moves that wouldn't occur to you in other sex positions.
Try wriggling against each other (pretend you're trying
to escape). Or try pelvic ripples or vibrations. Another
alternative – one that doesn't often happen during
intercourse – is to stay still. His erection may wane but
the challenge is to revive it using the power of erotic
suggestion (otherwise known as talking dirty).

wriggle
& writhe

TAKE A REST

As long as his penis can
take the unusual angle, you
could both try lying down
between each other's feet.
She can undulate her hips
while using her hand to
stroke her clitoris.

MIND SEX • SENSORY DEPRIVATION

One sex prop that can change the flavour of a sexual encounter instantly, bringing new and pleasurable sensations, is a blindfold. It takes you into an inner world of eroticism, face to face with the power of your own imagination.

Without sight you're forced to rely on your other senses – on smell, taste, touch and sound – to navigate your partner's body during fore-play and sex, and this will take you both to new and exciting pleasure zones. You may well find sex takes on a more intense dimension (read some of the sex scenes in *Blinding Light* by Paul Theroux for inspiration). Plus, if you're into domination and submission, a blindfold is an essential tool in your toy box. When your lover is blindfolded, become their "eyes" by describing what you're seeing in graphic detail.

Use a good-quality sleeping mask to blindfold your lover – not one that will slip down their face. A silk scarf wound round their head also works well. One of the most titillating ways to introduce a blindfold is by surprise – slip it on your lover during foreplay. But only do this if you know they'll respond well, and if you're in an established relationship – it's not the kind of trick you'd want to risk when you've only just met. If your lover wants to stop and remove the blindfold at any point, respect this.

A "BLIND" DATE

Five sexy things to do with a blindfold:
- Blindfold your lover and ply them with sensual and tactile treats to engage their senses, such as a sip of champagne or a piece of the darkest chocolate; a silk scarf wafted across their skin; your lips planting featherlight kisses on the tips of their fingers or the creases of their elbows; a dirty suggestion whispered in their ear; the smell of your skin as you press your body against theirs.
- Let your partner make love to you while you wear a blindfold. Take the chance to let go and just concentrate on all the non-visual aspects of sex. Note the way your partner touches you – is the touch soft, brisk, gentle, rough, or tender? How does each touch make you feel? You're likely to find it's a highly sensual and erotic lovemaking experience.
- Blindfold your partner and then "help yourself" to their naked body (with their prior permission, of course). Let their lack of sight disinhibit you – try out positions or techniques that might otherwise make you blush.
- Use a blindfold as a short cut to roleplaying. Once you've deprived your lover of sight, you can become anyone you want to be. You might even find it's easier to share sex secrets and fantasies (see pages 40–41) if you're not looking into each other's eyes.
- Blindfold your lover while they are standing up, then slowly undress them, pausing to kiss, suck, lick or stimulate them. Make it clear you're in charge. When they're naked and aroused, turn them round three times. Now hide somewhere and ask them to come and find you using touch alone.

TRY TANTRA • PLAYING THE FLUTE

As in many Tantric practices, the pleasure of this technique isn't immediately obvious. It involves sex, but not sex as you know it. Instead of pounding the mattress you'll be sitting in quiet – and ultimately ecstatic – connection with your lover. If you "play the flute" often, you'll come to understand the meaning of whole-body bliss. When you're both aroused, he sits on the floor or on a chair and she sits astride him and guides his penis into her. She pumps her love muscles (see pages 52–53) around him.

RAISING THE ENERGY

From now on instead of all the normal thrusting, bouncing and grinding of sex, you're going to stay almost completely still. Most of the movements you make will be internal. The only exception is if he loses his erection – in which case, use whatever technique you need to bring it back. Or if either of you find yourself about to come, pull back until your arousal level slips down a notch. The aim of the exercise is to channel sexual energy upward through your chakras (see pages 88–89) rather than to disperse it through orgasm.

Stage 1: Feel sexual energy building up in your pelvis. Inhale together, contracting your love muscles as you do so. Imagine that you're inhaling the air through your genitals. Feel your energy rise towards your sacral chakra. Now exhale together and let the energy flow back down and out of your inner flute. At the same time, relax your love muscles completely. Because there's a

lot going on simultaneously, you'll need to practise to keep it all synchronized. Your breath must be in sync with your love muscle movements, and you must both be in sync with each other throughout.

Stage 2: Once you're both in a rhythm, and feel confident drawing up energy to your sacral chakra and letting it go again, add the following visualization to the exercise. As you inhale and contract (keep "breathing in" through your genitals), imagine a bright white light at your base chakra that spirals up toward your sacral chakra. As you exhale-relax, picture the spiral of light moving back down your inner flute and out of your body. When you've practised this, imagine the spiral of light getting bigger so that it not only encompasses your own chakras but those of your partner too. In time you may find this brings a blissful sense of merging with each other.

Stage 3: Now use the combination of love-muscle contraction, breathing and visualization, to pull your sexual energy to the next chakra: the solar plexus chakra, just below your ribcage. Raise and lower the energy a few times. Now do the same with the heart chakra. In time, you can continue the exercise to the point where you raise and lower your energy to and from all the chakras. The techniques may feel mechanical, but as they become reflexive and you don't have to "think" so hard about them, you'll experience all-over delicious, tingling and expansive feelings.

LEG RAISE

In this position, you get all the pleasure of standing sex – immediacy, spontaneity, skin-to-skin contact and the chance to nuzzle and cuddle – but you don't risk falling over or injuring his back. She simply stands on one leg while he supports her raised thigh in his hand. He can make this position easier by squatting slightly.

sexy thrill

TONGUE PLAY

Before you begin, take it in turns to kneel and give each other some pre-sex oral attention. The more turned on you both are, the easier the Leg Raise will be.

MANDARIN DUCKS

For the most pleasurable start to the day, do this in the morning on a day when you don't have to go to work. Guys: cuddle behind her and mould yourself to her curves. Take things slowly – lightly run your hand along the curve of her hip and down her thigh, gently cup a breast in your palm and stroke her nipple with your thumb. Slip your hand between her legs – keep the mood slow and seductive. When she's ready to receive you, slide in slowly and stay still. Prop yourself on your elbow so you can see each other (this position allows the perfect combination of rear-entry intensity and face-to-face intimacy). Take your cues from her expression and body language.

MORNING SEX

Making love in the morning is great. The stresses of the day haven't yet kicked in; he may wake up with a handy erection; you're both relaxed and pliable from sleep; it gets your blood pumping; his testosterone levels, which control his libido, are higher in the morning than at any other time of day. There's no better feel-good way to start the day.

pure lust

PASSION-PLAY SEQUENCE

Try this sequence, from left to right, when your arousal levels are already at their peak. Begin in the Yawning Position, which allows instantly deep penetration. Next is the Packed Position in which she crosses one ankle over the other; she feels full and he feels squeezed. In the Rising Position she opens her legs wide, and he folds himself forward so you're chest to chest and cheek to cheek. It's one of the best positions for intimacy and passion – hold each other's hands and move. For the climax, she lowers her feet to the ground in Widely-Opened Position – this allows her more freedom of movement.

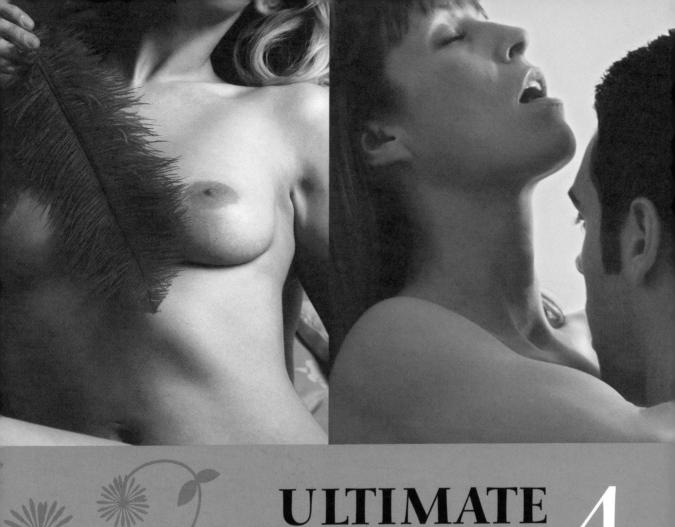

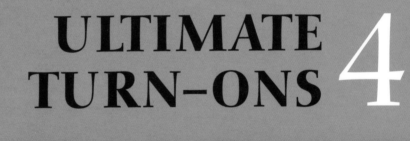

ULTIMATE
TURN-ONS 4

MUTUAL VIEW OF THE BUTTOCKS

This cheeky (literally!) sex position from *The Perfumed Garden* is a guaranteed turn-on. With his head propped up on a pillow, he gets a full-on view of one of his favourite parts of her, while watching the intimate ins and outs of sex as she bounces up and down on him. The rush for her comes from the fact that she knows she's turning him on.

SPINE-TINGLER

Guys: take this opportunity to draw your fingers down either side of her spine to give her wonderfully ecstatic goosebumps. The back is a much under-rated erogenous zone.

close desire

exotic erotic

TENTH POSITION

The thrill of this position is that it's meant to be a "just have to have you" headboard-bashing, mattress-pounding experience. Men were instructed to "place the woman on a low divan and tell her to grip the woodwork with her hands and your hips with her legs". After "introducing his member", the man is told to "grasp the divan" as well. Use this position for moments of urgent lust when you want to move freely and fast. The headboard will act as a buttress and shock absorber – you just have to hold on tight and enjoy the ride.

RAMPED-UP SEX

If you love positions like this where her bum is raised high in the air, a sex wedge can make it incredibly easy. A sex wedge is a type of sex prop (along with tilts, pads and boxes), which you position under your body during sex – it puts you at the perfect angle with zero effort on your part.

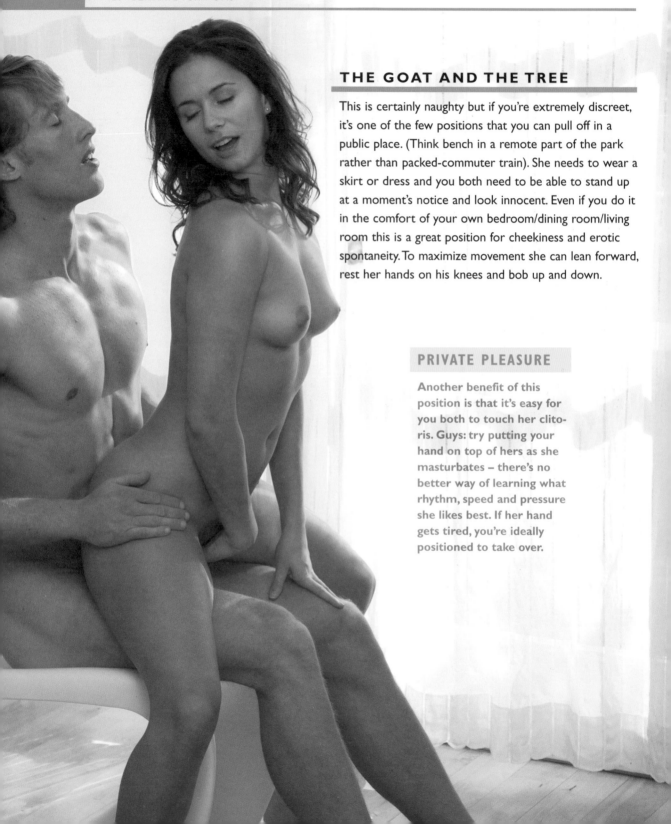

THE GOAT AND THE TREE

This is certainly naughty but if you're extremely discreet, it's one of the few positions that you can pull off in a public place. (Think bench in a remote part of the park rather than packed-commuter train). She needs to wear a skirt or dress and you both need to be able to stand up at a moment's notice and look innocent. Even if you do it in the comfort of your own bedroom/dining room/living room this is a great position for cheekiness and erotic spontaneity. To maximize movement she can lean forward, rest her hands on his knees and bob up and down.

PRIVATE PLEASURE

Another benefit of this position is that it's easy for you both to touch her clitoris. Guys: try putting your hand on top of hers as she masturbates – there's no better way of learning what rhythm, speed and pressure she likes best. If her hand gets tired, you're ideally positioned to take over.

DRIVING THE PEG HOME

There's no doubt about it — standing sex has erotic novelty but can be challenging. But the saving grace of this position is that she has the firm support of a wall behind her. So even if he's small and she's heavy, you both should be able to make it work. He should make sure he grips her firmly under the bum and she wraps her arms around his shoulders. Guys: the more you press her into the wall, the easier it will be to drive your peg home.

pump & grind

LOVE SWING

If you both love the idea of sex standing up but he finds it hard to take the weight, invest in a love swing. You hang it from the ceiling, she pops herself on the seat and gravity is no longer a problem.

KAMA SUTRA WISDOM · SEX TOOLS

Using sex toys is a great way to add variety to your foreplay and lovemaking, and find new ways to turn each other on. Men and women of Vatsyayana's time used sex toys too – but they were called "tools" rather than toys and, of course, they weren't as diverse, advanced or as multi-tasking as their 21st-century equivalents.

OLD-STYLE PLAY

Harem women were strictly guarded and not permitted to meet with men. They could have sex only when specifically visited for that purpose by their husband. And since one husband was shared by many women, a regular sex life couldn't be guaranteed. The solution to this was for women to dress up as men and service their fellow women with improvized sex toys.

Kama Sutra-style toys usually took the form of dildos that acted as a stand-in for a male erection. They were used by women on other women in the absence of men; or by men on women to satisfy their powerful sexual desires or to compensate for a flaccid penis. Dildos were made from gold, silver, copper, iron, ivory, buffalo horn, tin, lead or wood. Vatsyayana's opinion was that wood "more closely resembles the original". Also used were:

- Lubricant in the form of sesamum oil and herbal decoctions.
- Strings of beads wrapped around the penis.
- A cucumber attached to the hips with string.
- Penis sheaths attached to the man's waist in a harness.

SEX TOYS TODAY

There's no shame in sex toys – if you see them as last-resort props for a boring sex life, or just for lonely people, it's time for an attitude makeover. Think of sex toys as a way to extend your skills rather than to compensate for a lack of them. For example, if she's holding a vibrator against her clitoris, he can concentrate on her G-spot. Or if she uses a prostate massager on him, he'll experience newfound ecstasy when she then goes down on him. Or if he pops a vibrating love ring on his penis, you can both delight in hand-free clitoral stimulation. The list of opportunities goes on …

MIND SEX • VARIETY IS THE SPICE

Keep your arousal levels high and the passion alive by ensuring sex stays varied. It's something modern sexperts tell us and the ancient ones knew it, too. In the words of the *Ananga Ranga*: "The chief thing that drives men to the embraces of strange women, and women to the arms of strange men is the want of varied pleasures and the monotony that follows possession. Monotony brings about satiety and reluctance to engage in congress."

This doesn't mean you have to turn every sex session into an athletic marathon of positions (just do that every so often). But it does mean that you try to avoid following the same set of rote moves each time you have sex. And that you have different styles of sex to suit different moods. For example, sometimes you can have quickie sex – no preliminaries, no foreplay or romance – just clothes off and straight down to business. Sometimes you can have long, sensual sex in which you gaze into other's eyes, hold each other's face and bring each other slowly but surely to orgasm. Sometimes you have sex in which she leads and he does exactly what he's told to – at other times, he's the one in charge.

YOUR BAG OF SEX TRICKS

One of the easiest ways to introduce variety into your sex life is to stop thinking of sex merely as penetration. If you start devoting entire sessions to oral sex or to just manual sex, your love life will get an instant makeover. Another way to push the boundaries is to stop thinking

of sex as something that has to be reciprocal. If he's in the mood and she's not (or vice versa), it doesn't have to mean frustration or solitary masturbation for the frisky partner – delivering an unreciprocated hand job or oral pleasure is just as valid a form of sex as an hour's worth of intercourse. And if you're feeling too tired or too plain unsexy to do favours to a sex-hungry partner, try teamwork instead. For example – she cuddles or kisses him while he masturbates. Or he presses his fingers against her G-spot while she stimulates her clitoris. Imagine these are all moves in a bag of sex tricks – you can mix them up, personalize them and pull out whichever one or combination suits the occasion. The more options you have, the more alive, varied and versatile your relationship will be.

If you want true unpredictability in your sex life, play a variation of the dice game (as described in *The Dice Man* by Luke Rhinehart). Throw a dice three times to discover how you're going to have sex. Write down six options for each of the following:

- Foreplay (suggestions include: a five-minute snog, a 69 (see pages 100–101), or a genital massage (see pages 136–139).
- Sex positions (choose six at random from anywhere in this book).
- Venues (suggestions include: the sofa, the garden or the kitchen counter).

Throw the dice three times to decide the foreplay move, the sex position and the venue. Do exactly what the dice tells you to. No rethrows!

DRAGON TURN

Knowing the pleasure you're both getting from a sex position adds to the eroticism. In Dragon Turn the deep thrusting feels great all round – giving him excellent stimulation and her a fantastic full feeling. She lies on her back and uses her hands to spread her legs wide apart. He gets on all fours and enters her. This position allows for free thrusting because her legs are open wide. He should spend time moving in and out of the entrance to her vagina too, where her sensitive nerve endings lie.

JUST DO IT

A quick way to overhaul your sex life is to do it anywhere but the bedroom, and at a different time of day to usual. Dragon Turn is ideal for seduction on the sofa/chaise longue. Or do it on the floor when you just can't wait.

go in deep

RAINBOW ARCH

The distance and anonymity of this position makes it great for fantasizing during sex, and as he doesn't usually enter at this angle, it will feel excitingly novel. As well as experimenting with a new angle, you also get deep penetration plus a foot and shoulder massage (see below). The challenge is getting into the position. An easy way is to start in Cicada to the Side (see page 23), then she leans forward and clasps his ankles. He then guides her thighs around his so she's straddling him on her side.

dare to experiment

TOUCH ME ALL OVER

You can give each other whole-body shivers by combining sex with massage. He presses his fingers hard into the muscles of her shoulders; she caresses his legs and feet.

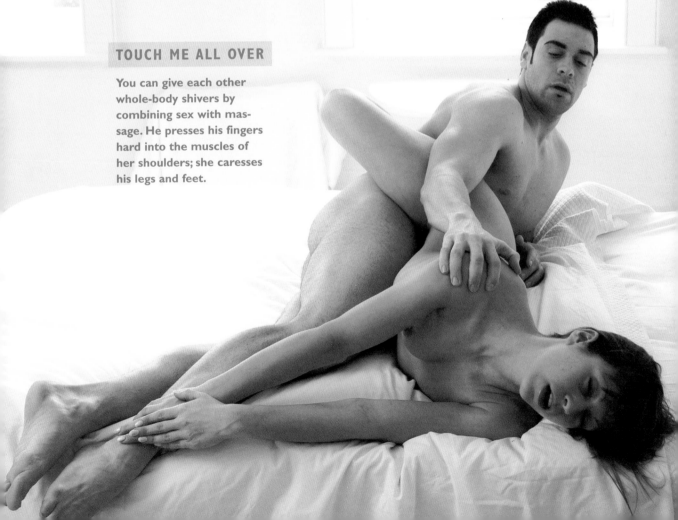

THE SWING

Girls: you get to turn him on here by taking charge. Straddle him cowgirl-style, with your back to him, then slowly lean forward so that you're resting on your hands and knees. The important bit is "slowly" – you're bending his penis away from its natural direction, so treat him with care. Now move your bum up and down, from side to side, or in circles. Go slowly at first to check he's OK with the movement, and to find out how far you can move without him slipping out.

slowly satisfy

FONDLE HER

Guys: if you're not too busy enjoying the view, you're in a prime position to stroke and massage her bum. Press your fingers, thumbs or even knuckles into her cheeks. With permission, you can even explore her anus and perineum very gently with your fingers.

TRY TANTRA • INVERTED BREATHING

Tantric sex isn't about providing fast thrills, but ultimately it can take your arousal levels sky-high. This exercise is the follow-on to Rocking Horse (see pages 64–65). You do it with your partner and, although there's no penetration involved, it feels incredibly intimate – some people say even more so than intercourse.

If you haven't yet done the rocking horse exercises on your own and with a partner, it's advisable to go back and do these first. If you don't, you might find there are too many unfamiliar techniques to co-ordinate all at once.

INHALE EACH OTHER

Take up your rocking horse positions (kneeling opposite each other with a firm cushion beneath your legs). Start rocking, separately at first and then in sync. Just to recap: inhale as you rock back, hold your breath briefly and then exhale as you rock forward. Now start to contract your love muscles (see pages 52–53) on the backward rock and release them on the forward rock. Keep your inhalations and exhalations in sync with these movements – practise this technique until it feels natural. In brief, what you need to remember is to "rock back-inhale-contract" and "rock forward-exhale-release".

Having learned to synchronize your breath, movement and love muscle contraction with your partner, you're now going to start doing the opposite to each other. As he rocks back, inhales and contracts, she rocks forward, exhales and relaxes. When it's your turn to exhale, imagine that the air is coming all the way up from your genitals along your inner flute (see pages 88–89). It's full of hot, tingling sexual energy and love. Blow this air on to your partner's lips and imagine that, through it, you're transferring a powerful erotic charge to them. Gaze at your partner.

When it's your turn to inhale, receive your partner's breath as they blow it towards you. Let it mingle with your own breath and pull it down deeply into your body – all the way down your inner flute to your genitals. You'll have your pelvis rocked back at this point and your love muscles contracted. Savour the feeling of having your partner's erotic energy swirling inside you. Maintain eye contact and get lost in the moment.

Once you have finished this exercise, close your eyes and sit quietly and still for a minute. Breathe normally and bring your attention to the inside of your body.

PERFORMANCE PRESSURE

Be prepared to practise the techniques in this and other Tantric exercises frequently. For the first few sessions you might find yourself thinking anything from: "Where's my pelvis supposed to be?" to "Why can't I feel anything yet?" to "My partner's better at this than I am". You're on a learning curve and as with any form of physical learning, you need to internalize the moves so that they become second nature to you. When this happens, you'll be able to give yourself up to sensation and benefit from a renewed intimacy and intensity in your lovemaking.

MIND SEX: GETTING INTO CHARACTER

You can get kinky and have great fun with some raunchy role-playing. The dressing-up element and the chance to "change" your character will add variety and be thrilling for both of you.

If you introduce sexual role-plays in the early days of your relationship, this will always stay open to you as a sexual option. Role-playing will be just another treat to pull out from your bag of sexual tricks, whenever you or your partner are in the mood.

PICK YOUR ROLE

The stereotypical sexual role-play consists of the woman dressed as a naughty schoolgirl with the man in full headmaster costume disciplining her until she promises to be good. If this doesn't appeal to you, reinvent the roles in ways that do. But bear in mind that the dominance and submission of all the common role-plays (think master/slave, prisoner/guard, doctor/patient) are an important part of the mix. Choosing egalitarian roles, such as office co-workers, doesn't really work (unless you're having a secret affair with the person who sits at the desk opposite!).

Introducing power differences in the form of role-play can release you from all the constraints of everyday equitable sex. You might find your mind is less occupied with thoughts about whether your partner is having a good time, whether you are going to come too quickly, too slowly or not at all, or even whether you look OK. In short, it frees you from your normal self – you can be bold, bossy, domineering, shy,

submissive, coy or vulnerable. You can trade in your entire personality for a new one – and you don't need to feel inhibited, because your partner's doing exactly the same thing.

ACTING IT OUT

If you're new to role-playing, try these tips:
• Dress up. The clothes will transform your behaviour, not just your appearance.
• If you decide that dressing up isn't for you or you've left your "wardrobe" at home, a blindfold is a good way of opening the door to a new sexual persona.
• You don't have to enter the world of ropes, handcuffs and dungeons (unless you want to). You can wield power in a role-play by withholding sexual favours or arousing your partner to the point of climax and then pulling back.
• If you want to experiment with inflicting pain on your partner, ask permission first and stick to mild forms, such as spanking (see pages 86–87) or using nipple clamps.
• If you're the one wielding the power, play up to your role. This is your chance to be the boss – enjoy it. Take charge of the situation and tell your lover exactly what you want them to do (and what they're not allowed to do).
• If you're the submissive party, discover the joy of surrender by completely letting go. Allow yourself to become truly weak and vulnerable – if you're normally tough or even aggressive in your everyday life, you might find it surprisingly cathartic to behave this way.

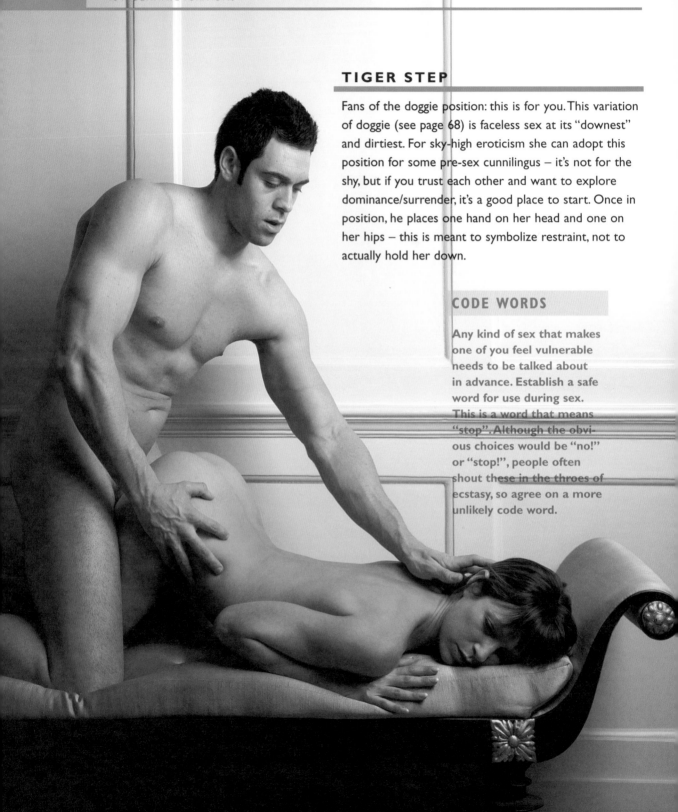

TIGER STEP

Fans of the doggie position: this is for you. This variation of doggie (see page 68) is faceless sex at its "downest" and dirtiest. For sky-high eroticism she can adopt this position for some pre-sex cunnilingus – it's not for the shy, but if you trust each other and want to explore dominance/surrender, it's a good place to start. Once in position, he places one hand on her head and one on her hips – this is meant to symbolize restraint, not to actually hold her down.

CODE WORDS

Any kind of sex that makes one of you feel vulnerable needs to be talked about in advance. Establish a safe word for use during sex. This is a word that means "stop". Although the obvious choices would be "no!" or "stop!", people often shout these in the throes of ecstasy, so agree on a more unlikely code word.

SITTING-ON-TOP POSITION

She turns on herself and him in this position. The *Ananga Ranga* says it's for women whose "lust has not yet been sated". He lies back and she sits on top of him in a cross-legged position. The fact that neither lover can move very much doesn't matter – it's an opportunity for her to feel his length and girth inside her as she stimulates her clitoris with her fingers. It feels fantastic for her and he gets the eroticism of being a voyeur, plus some delicious contractions around his penis as she comes.

TAKING THE WEIGHT

Girls: if you're in danger of crushing him by sitting cross legged, find a way of modifying this position: take some of your weight on one hand or keep one foot on the bed. Or, if you're very supple, lean back so that you're lying in between his legs.

SENSUAL PLEASURE • SIZZLING MASSAGE FOR HER

Turn her on with some toe-tingling, out-of-this world touch techniques. Unlike intercourse, which can miss the clitoral area, this massage makes her clitoris the key player. Your checklist of essential ingredients is: a warm pair of hands, some water-based lube and plenty of time.

WHAT TO DO

Step 1: Move your palm in small, slow circles around her navel, gradually taking in her pubic area. Keep your touch light. If she's got pubic hair, run your fingers lightly through it and tug it slightly. Use your fingertips to lightly brush and tickle from her pubic triangle along the length of her vulva to her perineum. Press the flat of your hand against her so the heel is pressing on her clitoris and your fingers are pointing towards her anus. Move your fingers in a rippling motion (a bit like you're drumming them softly on a table).

Step 2: Using your index finger, trace a line that starts above her clitoral hood, goes down to her vagina and then back up again – imagine you're drawing an elongated oval. Vary the pressure as you go to see what kind of touch she finds most arousing. Gradually make the elongated oval shorter and shorter so that you zone in on her clitoral hood. Draw circles around it. Again vary the pressure and also the speed. Keep your finger well lubed and keep watching her responses – if she likes what you're doing, settle into a steady speed and rhythm. Too much variety and too many changes of pace can distract her.

Step 3: Keep circling her clitoral hood, but gradually move in to touch her clitoral head – this is the epicentre of erotic sensation and some women find being touched here too intense. If she can take it, move the tip of your finger rapidly from side to side across her clitoral head. If she prefers a more indirect touch, lay the pads of three fingertips across her clitoral head and hood and moving them from side to side – find a pressure and a speed that you can keep up.

Let your partner decide how she wants the massage to end – it could be a body-shaking orgasm or a cuddle, or she may want you inside her.

SENSUAL PLEASURE • SIZZLING MASSAGE FOR HIM

He will love to be "handled" by you, especially if you initiate his arousal and take charge of the pleasure. While he'll know what he likes and how he wants to be touched, embrace the idea that you're offering him something unique and special, something that only you can deliver. Forget the word "hand job" and think erotic massage instead. And although he'll probably be able to come quickly, don't make his orgasm your immediate aim; instead, explore, enjoy and see what happens … his role is to relax and enjoy.

Apart from a pair of confident hands, you also need a lubricant to make your fingers slip, slide and glide against him. If there's a possibility you're going to have sex later, choose a water-based lube. This won't damage latex condoms and it won't upset the delicate environment of your vagina. Otherwise, you can use oil or an oil-based lube – this has the advantage of being incredibly slippery. It's also a good idea to keep a box of tissues handy for clean-up (even though his ejaculation isn't your main aim).

WHAT TO DO

Step 1: Get your partner to lie down or lean back on a bank of pillows and then stroke his whole genital area using well-lubed hands. Use a flat hand-over-hand technique so you start on his perineum and then glide one hand after another over his balls and up along the length of his shaft. Keep your strokes slow, firm and heavy. The best position for doing this is facing his feet – you can either straddle his chest or kneel beside him.

Step 2: Once he's erect or semi-erect, place one hand on the underside of his shaft, pressing it gently into his belly. Use your other hand to massage his perineum – use firm fingertip pressure – the pads of your fingers should move the muscles below his skin in firm circles (no fingernails though). Concentrate particularly on his external P-spot (see pages 70–71).

Step 3: Now change position so you're straddling or sitting beside his legs and facing his head. Re-lube your hands and place them around his penis so that your fingers are interlocked around his shaft. Your thumbs should rest on the underside of his penis so that he feels firmly enclosed. Slowly glide your hands up and down his penis, pressing on his frenulum with your thumbs as you pass. You can also use undulating pressure from your palms as you go.

Step 4: Stay in the position you're in and make rings around his penis using the thumb and fingers of each hand. Glide the rings up and down his shaft and head. Once you've got into a rhythm, start twisting the rings in opposite directions as you go. Keep varying your pressure too – say, five firm up-and-down strokes, five gentle, and so on …

Ask him how he'd like to end the massage – you can make him come if it feels right, you can climb on top if him or you can extend the massage to include his internal P-spot (see pages 70–71).

THE TURNING POSITION

Take your lovemaking to the next level with this bold and athletic position. And the great thing about it is if you don't pull it off, you can still have fun and enjoy giggling about it. Before you start you'll need plenty of lube plus a strong erection. He starts off in the missionary position and then turns by 180 degrees so that he's facing her feet. The tricky bit is that his penis must remain inside her for the duration of the turn (see left).

SKILFUL SEX

Guys: make the turn in small stages and withdraw a little, but not completely, as you turn – this makes it easier to manoeuvre. If you feel your erection waning, thrust to get it back again.

turn her on

LOTUS POSITION

He'll love to look at her as she lies on her back with her legs in the lotus position, opening herself to him. He penetrates from on top. It's challenging, but will be thrilling for both of you. The lotus position binds her legs in position and, once his body is pressing down on hers, she's effectively locked into place. Girls: practise getting in to the lotus position (see below) on your own before you attempt it in bed with your lover. If she can't achieve this, she should cross her legs as shown here.

GET IN POSITION

Girls: to get in the lotus position, sit with your back straight, the soles of your feet pressed together and your knees out to the sides. Bounce your knees up and down, so you feel a stretch in your groin. Bend your right leg and tuck your right heel into your left groin. Lift your left heel into your lap and tuck it in as closely as you can to your right groin.

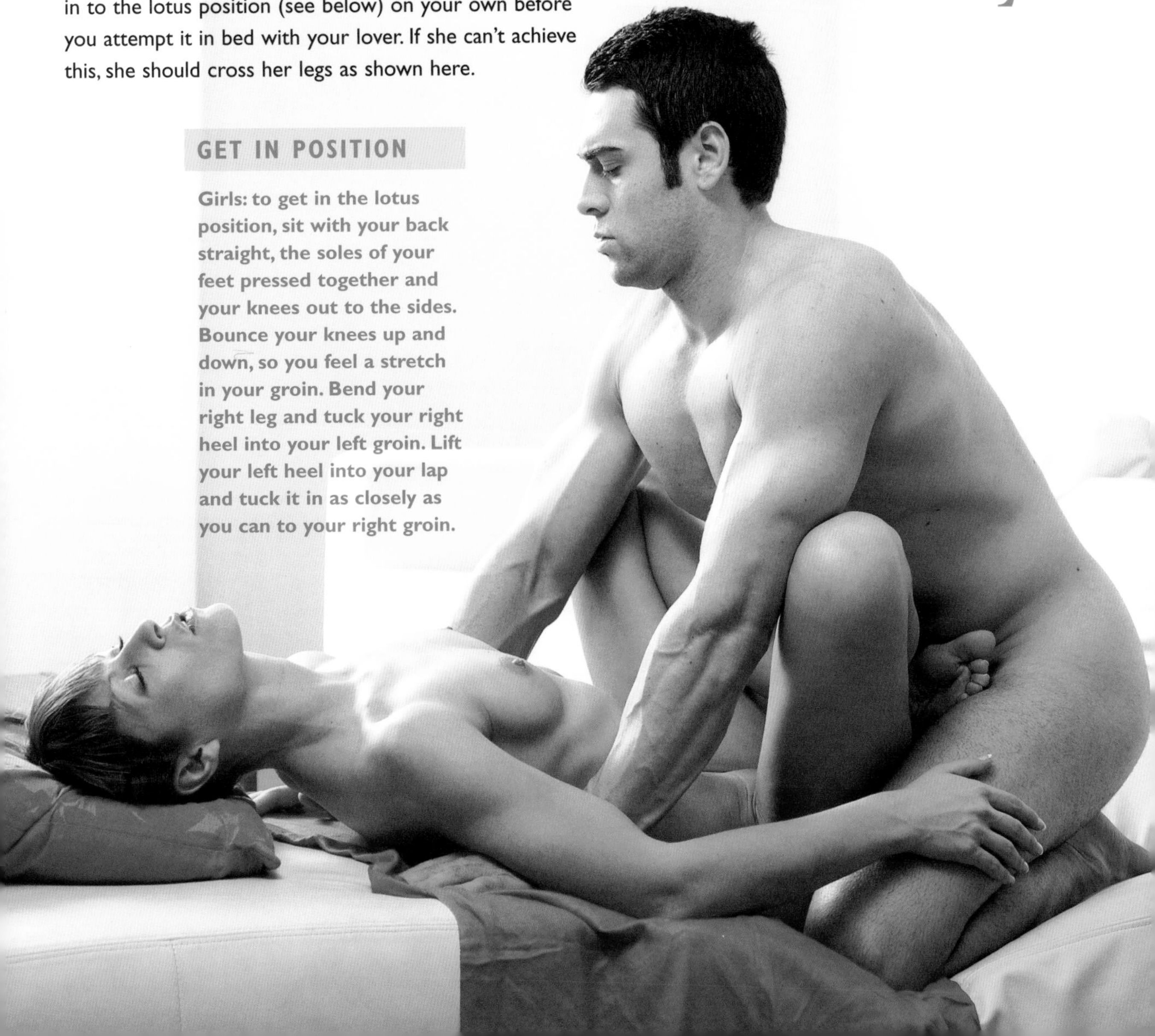

get
kinky

TRY TANTRA • MERGING THROUGH BREATH

Being totally at one with your partner can be incredibly arousing. The following technique is described as a delicious dance of breath, energy and light. If you practise it often, it'll become an ecstatic way of joining with your partner, but before you try it, practise the other Tantric exercises in this book.

ASSUME POSITIONS

Get into a Tantric embrace position – he sits on the floor with his legs parted and she sits astride him so that they can hug each other. However, he doesn't have to be inside her; sitting in this embrace position will mean the genitals are in contact, but there is no penetration.

Stage 1: Start rocking your pelvises backward and forward like you did in Rocking Horse (see pages 64–65). Take the tingling, erotic feeling in your genitals and pull it up your inner flute – like you did in Playing the Flute (see pages 110–111). Gaze into each other's eyes. Feel your sexual energy expanding and connecting you. If you're in an easy flowing rhythm and can sense the energy moving inside you, move on to the next stage.

Stage 2: Still in the embrace position, start to kiss – a deep, passionate, mouth-to-mouth kiss. Keep your lips together and begin inverted breathing. The technique is the same as the inverted breathing technique (see pages 130–131), but instead of blowing on each other's lips, you exhale straight into your lover's mouth.

Ultimately, you're going to combine rocking, love muscle contraction and breathing, but because this is a novel way of breathing, it helps to practise it on its own first. She exhales into his mouth and he pulls her breath all the way down his inner flute to his genitals. Then he pulls his energy back up and exhales into her mouth.

Now bring in the pelvic rocking and love muscle contractions. He rocks forward, exhales into her mouth and relaxes his love muscles, while she rocks back, inhales his breath and contracts her love muscles. Let sexual feelings permeate your whole body. Enjoy it.

KAMA SUTRA WISDOM • THE END OF CONGRESS

The hope is that you're fully turned on and tired out from a super-session of lovemaking. Make it special right to the end by coming down from sex slowly and sensually together. According to the *Kama Sutra,* the end of sex should be as sensual and attentive as the beginning. So, if following sex you and your partner are in the habit of jumping out of bed, falling asleep or turning on the television, try lying in each other's arms instead. The ideal positions for doing this are the spoons position or a woman-on-top position (as long as she's not too heavy).

Once you're both fully pleasured, hold each other and let your breathing gradually slow down. Synchronize your breathing with your lover's until you are both taking deep relaxed belly breaths in perfect harmony. You may be in a state of deep relaxation, but try to stay present with your lover. Enjoy the altered state of consciousness that sex can bring. Observe any images or fantasies that drift through your mind. Whisper them to your partner if you feel like it. Concentrate on the warm, loving feelings you have for your partner. Imagine that you're wrapped in a cocoon of light.

AFTER THE CLIMAX

The following extracts from the *Kama Sutra* describe the rituals couples should follow after lovemaking: "When their passion has ceased, the two lovers, showing modesty, and without looking at each other, should go to wash separately. Then, sitting in their own places, they should eat

some betel leaves. The man should rub an ointment, such as pure sandalwood ointment into
his lover's skin. Then he should embrace her
with his left arm and encourage her to drink
from a cup that he holds in his hand. The couple
can eat sweetmeats; they can drink fresh juice,
soup, gruel, extracts of meat, sherbet, the juice of
mango fruit, the extract of the juice of the citron
tree mixed with sugar, or anything that may be
enjoyed in different countries. The man tastes
each food first and tells the woman whether it is
sweet, delicate or soft before passing it to her.

The couple may sit in the terrace or on the
rooftop of the house or palace and talk of pleas-
ant things. The woman may lie with her head in
the man's lap and her face towards the moon.
The man may point out the different stars and
name them – for example, the Pole Star and the
garland of Seven Sages that form the Great Bear.
This is the end of congress."

THE ARTFUL ENDING

The *Ananga Ranga* also recommends a dignified
end to sex. Its advice to men is: "When your
amorous frolics are at an end, take care not to
get up brusquely. Instead, gently withdraw your
member and stay with your lover. Lie on your
right side in the bed of pleasure. In this way you
won't resemble a man who mounts a woman like
mule and pays no attention to the art of love.
Withdrawing and hurrying away as soon as you
have ejaculated is a crude approach that deprives
the woman of all pleasure."

ride him

BUTTERFLY

Butterfly is a thrilling, erotic display. She sits with her knees bent and her legs either side of him. She can slide backwards and forwards, wiggle her hips from side to side, lifts herself a little way up his shaft and shake her bottom. Or the move that men find sexiest: she can raise and lower herself slowly along his shaft while opening her legs wide so that he can see what's going on.

THE CLIMAX

If you want to get closer for the climax, he can sit up and hold her in his arms. What you lose in movement you make up for in the intimacy of full-body contact.

52

CONGRESS OF A COW

It's simple: she bends over and he penetrates. For fast, spontaneous, dirty sex it can't be beaten. The drawbacks of this position are: a) he'll come too soon (the sight of her raised bum plus complete freedom of movement may prove too much for him); b) she may find it uncomfortable, especially if he's got a large penis. The solutions to both are: take it slowly and talk to each other while you're doing it (an "mmmmmm" or a "slower!" will do the job from her; and an "OK?" will be appreciated from him). Also, loads of lube on her vaginal entrance and his penis will help to make the friction smooth and slick.

ANONYMOUS SEX

Although it's criticized for its lack of intimacy, having sex in a position where you can't see each other's face has its virtues. It leaves you free to concentrate on your own pleasure because you're not distracted trying to read your partner's facial or bodily cues. This can be particularly good for women who find it difficult to reach orgasm during intercourse.

ramp it up

DOWN AND DIRTY SEQUENCE

Try this sequence, from left to right, starting with the raunchy anonymity of The Swing, which allows for some wild fantasizing and concentration on what feels good. Then the tempo is turned down slightly by moving into Mutual View of the Buttocks – she's still facing away from him but in a more sedate, upright sitting position. Next comes the tricky manoeuvre of turning to face him. (Girls: you need to swivel 180 degrees. If it's too tricky, dismount before climbing back on in the Sitting-On-Top Position.) Finally, she puts her feet on either side of his body and leans back to clasp his legs in Butterfly.

FURTHER READING

BOOKS TO READ:

Anand, Margot *The New Art of Sexual Ecstasy* (Thorsons, 2003)

Anand, Margot and Johncock, Philip D. *The Sexual Ecstasy Workbook* (Deep Books, 2005)

Angler, Natalie *Woman: An Intimate Geography* (Virago Press, 2000)

Bailey, Nicole *69 Ways to Please Your Lover* (Duncan Baird Publishers, 2004)

Bailey, Nicole *Pocket Erotic* (Duncan Baird Publishers, 2008)

Bailey, Nicole *Pure Erotic Massage* (Duncan Baird Publishers, 2007)

Bailey, Nicole *Pure Kama Sutra* (Duncan Baird Publishers, 2005)

Bailey, Nicole *The Pocket Kama Sutra* (Duncan Baird Publishers, 2006)

Blue, Violet *The Ultimate Guide to Sexual Fantasy* (Cleis Press, 2004)

Burton, Sir Richard F. and Arbuthnot, Forster F. (translators) *The Illustrated Kama Sutra, Ananga Ranga, Perfumed Garden* (Hamlyn, 1996)

Doniger, Wendy and Kakar, Sudhir (translators) *Kamasutra* (Oxford University Press, 2002)

Douglass, Marcia and Douglass, Lisa *The Sex You Want* (Da Capo Press, 2002)

Em & Lo *Sex – How to do Everything* (Dorling Kindersley, 2008)

Friday, Nancy *Men in Love* (Delta, 1998)

Friday, Nancy *My Secret Garden* (Quartet Books, 2001)

Hite, Shere *The New Hite Report* (Seven Stories Press, 2003)

Hooper, Anne *Pure Sex* (Duncan Baird Publishers, 2003)

Semans, Anne & Winks, Cathy *The New Good Vibrations Guide to Sex* (Cleis Press, 1997)

Winks, Cathy *The Good Vibrations Guide: The G-Spot* (Down There Press, 1998)

WEBSITES TO BROWSE:
LoveHoney.co.uk
EmotionalBliss.com
AnnSummers.com
The-Clitoris.com

INDEX

Author's acknowledgments
Thanks to Grace Cheetham, Dawn Bates, Manisha Patel and Saskia Janssen at Duncan Baird Publishers.

Publisher's acknowledgments
The publisher's would like to thank:
Photography: John Davies (represented by Soho Management)
Photographic assistant: Dave Foster
Make up artist: Nadine Wilkie
Models: supplied by International Models Management (IMM), London